*Second-Order Partial Differential Equations*

M. M. SMIRNOV

# Second-Order Partial Differential Equations

*Edited by*
S. CHOMET,
King's College, London
*Translated by*
Scripta Technica Ltd.

1966

NOORDHOFF · GRONINGEN · THE NETHERLANDS

# FOREWORD TO THE RUSSIAN EDITION

This book was written as a textbook for engineering and physics students and deals with the theory of second-order partial differential equations – a branch of mathematics extensively applied to the solution of many varied problems in mechanics, physics and engineering. It begins with the derivation of the basic equations of mathematical physics and with their classification. This is followed by a systematic account of the theory of hyperbolic, parabolic and elliptic equations, and also of the potential theory. The methods of characteristics and of Fourier and Green functions are then discussed in connection with second-order partial differential equations. The material provided is suitable as a first introduction to this subject. The author wishes to thank Academician V. I. Smirnov and Professor S. G. Mikhlin, who read the manuscript, for many valuable suggestions.

M. M. Smirnov

Leningrad, January 20, 1964

# CONTENTS

# INTRODUCTION

An equation relating an unknown function $u(x_1, \ldots, x_n)$, the independent variables $x_1, \ldots, x_n$ and the partial derivatives of the unknown function is called a *partial differential equation*. It may be written in the form

$$F\left(x_1, x_2, \ldots, x_n, u, \frac{\partial u}{\partial x_1}, \ldots, \frac{\partial u}{\partial x_n}, \ldots\right.$$

$$\left. \ldots, \frac{\partial^k u}{\partial x_1^{k_1} \ldots \partial x_n^{k_n}}, \ldots\right) = 0, \tag{1}$$

where $F$ is a given function of its arguments.

The *order* of a partial differential equation is that of the derivative of highest order.

The most general first-order partial differential equation with two independent variables $x$ and $y$ may be written in the form

$$F(x, y, u, p, q) = 0 \quad \left(p = \frac{\partial u}{\partial x}, q = \frac{\partial u}{\partial y}\right). \tag{2}$$

Similarly, the most general second-order partial differential equation is of the form

$$F(x, y, u, p, q, r, s, t) = 0 \left(r = \frac{\partial^2 u}{\partial x^2}, s = \frac{\partial^2 u}{\partial x \partial y}, t = \frac{\partial^2 u}{\partial y^2}\right). \tag{3}$$

A partial differential equation is called *quasi-linear* if it is *linear* in all the highest-order derivatives of the unknown function. For example, the equation

$$A(x, y, u, u_x, u_y) \frac{\partial^2 u}{\partial x^2} + B(\ldots) \frac{\partial^2 u}{\partial x \partial y} +$$

$$+ C(\ldots) \frac{\partial^2 u}{\partial y^2} + f(x, y, u, u_x, u_y) = 0 \tag{4}$$

is a quasi-linear second-order equation.

A partial differential equation is called *linear* if it is linear in the unknown function and its partial derivatives. For example, the equation

$$A(x, y) \frac{\partial^2 u}{\partial x^2} + 2B(x, y) \frac{\partial^2 u}{\partial x \partial y} + C(x, y) \frac{\partial^2 u}{\partial y^2} +$$

$$+ D(x, y) \frac{\partial u}{\partial x} + E(x, y) \frac{\partial u}{\partial y} + G(x, y)u = F(x, y) \quad (5)$$

is a second-order linear equation in the unknown function $u(x, y)$. The *solution* of the partial differential equation (1) is any function $u = u(x_1, \ldots, x_n)$ which when substituted for the unknown function and into the derivatives converts this equation into an identity in the independent variables.

In this text we shall be mainly concerned with second-order linear equations, and especially the *wave equation*

$$\frac{\partial^2 u}{\partial t^2} = a^2 \left( \frac{\partial^2 u}{\partial x^2} + \frac{\partial^2 u}{\partial y^2} + \frac{\partial^2 u}{\partial z^2} \right), \quad (6)$$

the *Laplace equation*

$$\frac{\partial^2 u}{\partial x^2} + \frac{\partial^2 u}{\partial y^2} + \frac{\partial^2 u}{\partial z^2} = 0 \quad (7)$$

and the *heat-transfer equation*

$$\frac{\partial u}{\partial t} = a^2 \left( \frac{\partial^2 u}{\partial x^2} + \frac{\partial^2 u}{\partial y^2} + \frac{\partial^2 u}{\partial z^2} \right). \quad (8)$$

Many problems in physics and technology may be reduced to partial differential equations and in particular to equations (6), (7), and (8).

Chapter 1

DERIVATION OF THE FUNDAMENTAL EQUATIONS OF
MATHEMATICAL PHYSICS

§ 1. Vibrations of a string

Consider a stretched string fixed at each end. The string will be
assumed to be *thin* and *flexible*, i.e. we shall assume that it offers
no resistance to any change of form other than a change of length.
The tension $T_0$ in the string will be assumed to be much greater
than the gravitational forces acting upon it, so that the latter can
be neglected.
Suppose that in equilibrium the string is parallel to the $x$-axis. We
shall confine our attention to transverse vibrations, assuming that
the motion occurs in a plane, and that the elements of the string
move at right angles to the $x$-axis.
Let $u(x, t)$ represent the displacement of the string at time $t$ from
the position of equilibrium. For each fixed value of $t$ the function
$u(x, t)$ will clearly represent the form of the string (fig. 1).
Let us suppose further that the vibrations are *small*, so that the
displacement $u(x, t)$ and the derivative $\partial u/\partial x$ are so small that their
squares and products can be neglected.
Consider an arbitrary segment $(x_1, x_2)$ of the string (see fig. 1) which
is deformed into the segment $M_1 M_2$ as a result of the vibration.
The length of the arc $M_1 M_2$ at time $t$ is

$$S' = \int_{x_1}^{x_2} \sqrt{1 + u_x^2}\, dx \approx x_2 - x_1 = S,$$

so that for small vibrations there is no change in the length of a
given segment. In view of Hooke's law, the tension $T$ at each point
in the string is independent of time. Under the above assumptions,
the change in the tension during the motion of the string can be
neglected in comparison with the tension in equilibrium.
We shall show that the tension $T$ can be regarded as independent
of $x$, that is, $T \approx T_0$. In fact, the forces acting on the segment

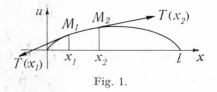

Fig. 1.

$M_1M_2$ are the tensions at $M_1$ and $M_2$ which are tangential to the string, the external forces (if any), and the inertial forces. The $x$-component of the resultant of all these forces must be equal to zero, and since we are considering only transverse vibrations, the inertial and external forces are parallel to the $u$-axis and

$$T(x_1) \cos \alpha(x_1) - T(x_2) \cos \alpha(x_2) = 0,$$

where $\alpha(x)$ is the angle between the tangent at the point $x$ at time $t$ and the positive direction of the $x$-axis.
Since the oscillations are small, we have

$$\cos \alpha(x) = \frac{1}{\sqrt{1 + \tan^2 \alpha(x)}} = \frac{1}{\sqrt{1 + u_x^2}} \approx 1$$

and hence

$$T(x_1) \approx T(x_2).$$

Since $x_1$ and $x_2$ are arbitrary, the magnitude of $T$ is independent of $x$. We have thus shown that $T \approx T_0$ for all $x$ and $t$.
Let us consider the derivation of the equation for the vibrations of a string. We shall make use of *d'Alambert's principle*, which requires that the forces acting on a given segment of the string, including inertial forces, shall be in equilibrium.
Consider an arbitrary segment $M_1M_2$ of the string, and let us set up the condition which will ensure that the sum of the components of all forces acting on the segment in the direction of the $u$-axis is zero. Thus, the sum of the components of the tension at $M_1$ and $M_2$ in the direction of the $u$-axis is

$$Y = T_0[\sin \alpha(x_2) - \sin \alpha(x_1)],$$

but in view of the above assumptions

$$\sin \alpha(x) = \frac{\tan \alpha(x)}{\sqrt{1 + \tan^2 \alpha(x)}} = \frac{\dfrac{\partial u}{\partial x}}{\sqrt{1 + \left(\dfrac{\partial u}{\partial x}\right)^2}} \approx \frac{\partial u}{\partial x}$$

and therefore

$$Y = T_0 \left[ \left(\frac{\partial u}{\partial x}\right)_{x=x_2} - \left(\frac{\partial u}{\partial x}\right)_{x=x_1} \right].$$

Since

$$\left(\frac{\partial u}{\partial x}\right)_{x=x_2} - \left(\frac{\partial u}{\partial x}\right)_{x=x_1} = \int_{x_1}^{x_2} \frac{\partial^2 u}{\partial x^2}\, dx,$$

we finally have

$$Y = T_0 \int_{x_1}^{x_2} \frac{\partial^2 u}{\partial x^2}\, dx. \tag{1.1}$$

Let $p(x, t)$ be the external force per unit mass acting on the string in the direction of the $u$-axis. The component of the external force acting on the segment $M_1 M_2$ in the direction of the $u$-axis will then be

$$\int_{x_1}^{x_2} p(x, t)\, dx. \tag{1.2}$$

If $\rho(x)$ is the linear density of the string, then the inertial force on the segment $M_1 M_2$ is

$$- \int_{x_1}^{x_2} \rho(x) \frac{\partial^2 u}{\partial t^2}\, dx. \tag{1.3}$$

The sum of the components given by (1.1), (1.2) and (1.3) must be equal to zero, i.e.

$$\int_{x_1}^{x_2} \left[ T_0 \frac{\partial^2 u}{\partial x^2} - \rho(x) \frac{\partial^2 u}{\partial t^2} + p(x, t) \right] dx = 0.$$

and since $x_1$ and $x_2$ are arbitrary, it follows that the integrand must vanish for all $x$ and $t$, that is:

$$\rho(x)\,\frac{\partial^2 u}{\partial t^2} = T_0\,\frac{\partial^2 u}{\partial x^2} + p(x, t). \tag{1.4}$$

This is the required differential equation for the vibrations of the string.

When $\rho = $ const, i.e. when the string is uniform, equation (1.4) is usually written in the form

$$\frac{\partial^2 u}{\partial t^2} = a^2\,\frac{\partial^2 u}{\partial x^2} + f(x, t), \tag{1.5}$$

where

$$a = \sqrt{\frac{T_0}{\rho}}, \quad f(x, t) = \frac{p(x, t)}{\rho}. \tag{1.6}$$

If there are no external forces we have $p(x, t) = 0$, and the equation of free oscillations of the string becomes

$$\frac{\partial^2 u}{\partial t^2} = a^2\,\frac{\partial^2 u}{\partial x^2}. \tag{1.7}$$

Equation (1.4) has an infinite number of special solutions, and therefore in itself is insufficient for the complete determination of the motion of a string; certain additional conditions determined by the physical aspects of the problem must be specified. It is known from particle dynamics that the initial position and the initial velocity of a particle are necessary for the determination of its motion. In the case of the oscillations of a string it is natural to specify the position and a velocity of all points of the string at time $t = 0$:

$$u|_{t=0} = \varphi_0(x), \quad \frac{\partial u}{\partial t}\bigg|_{t=0} = \varphi_1(x). \tag{1.8}$$

The latter conditions are called the *initial conditions*.

Moreover, since the string is supposed to have a finite length, it is necessary to specify the conditions at its ends. If the ends are fixed, we have

$$u|_{x=0} = 0, \quad u|_{x=l} = 0 \tag{1.9}$$

for any $t \geqslant 0$. The conditions given by (1.9) are called *boundary conditions*. Other boundary conditions are also possible.

We have thus reduced the physical problem of the oscillations of a string to a mathematical problem, in which we require to find the particular solution of equation (1.4) which satisfies the initial conditions given by (1.8) and the boundary conditions given by (1.9). It is possible to consider a *semi-infinite* or an *infinite* string when one or both ends of the string are at infinity. Both these cases are idealisations of a very long string. The first corresponds to cases where one is concerned with points near one of the ends of the string, whilst the second is important in connection with points at large distances from both ends. The boundary condition $u|_{x=0} = 0$ remains for the first of these cases, while in the second there are no boundary conditions at all. The initial functions $\varphi_0(x)$ and $\varphi_1(x)$ must then be specified respectively for all $0 \leqslant x < \infty$ or for all $-\infty < x < \infty$.

## § 2. Oscillations of a membrane

A *membrane* is defined as a *perfectly flexible stretched sheet*.

Let us suppose that in equilibrium the membrane lies in the $x, y$-plane and occupies a region $D$ bounded by a closed curve $L$. Next, we shall suppose that the membrane is under the action of a uniform tension $T$ applied at its edges. This means that if we draw a line on the membrane in any direction, the force between the two parts separated by an element of the line is proportional to the length of the element, and is perpendicular to its direction; the force acting on an element $ds$ of the line will be equal to $T\,ds$.

We shall confine our attention to transverse oscillations of the membrane in which each of its points moves along the $u$-axis which is perpendicular to the $x, y$-plane. The displacement $u$ of a point $x, y$ on the membrane will then be a function of $x, y$, and $t$.

Moreover, we shall restrict our analysis to small oscillations and will suppose that the function $u(x, y, t)$ and its partial derivatives with respect to $x$ and $y$ are small so that their squares and products can be neglected.

Consider an arbitrary area $\sigma$ of the membrane which in equilibrium is bounded by a curve $l$. When the membrane is displaced from the position of equilibrium, this part of the membrane will be deformed into an area $\sigma'$ bounded by a space curve $l'$. At time $t$ the area $\sigma'$ is given by

$$\sigma' = \iint_{\sigma} \sqrt{1 + u_x^2 + u_y^2}\, dx\, dy \approx \iint_{\sigma} dx\, dy = \sigma.$$

Therefore, subject to our assumptions, we can neglect the change in $\sigma$ during the oscillations and consider that the tension in the membrane is constant and equal to the initial value $T$.

We shall now derive the equation of transverse oscillations of a membrane. Consider an arbitrary area $\sigma'$ of the membrane. The tension $T$ which is perpendicular to the contour $l'$ at all its points lies in the tangent plane to the surface. Let $ds'$ be an element of the curve $l'$ so that the tension acting on this element is $T\,ds'$. The cosine of the angle between the tension vector $\boldsymbol{T}$ and the $u$-axis is, in view of our assumptions, equal to $\partial u/\partial n$, where $\partial/\partial n$ represents differentiation along the outward normal to the curve $l$ which bounds the area $\sigma$ in the position of equilibrium (fig. 2). It follows that the component of the tensile force acting on the element $ds'$ in the direction of the $u$-axis is

$$T\, \frac{\partial u}{\partial n}\, ds'$$

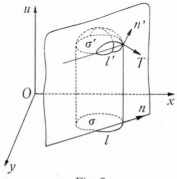

Fig. 2

so that the component along the $u$-axis of the resultant force acting on the contour $l'$ is equal to

$$T \int_{l'} \frac{\partial u}{\partial n} \, ds'. \tag{2.1}$$

Since for small oscillations we can let $ds \approx ds'$, the path of integration in (2.1) may be replaced by $l$ and hence, using Green's formula, we obtain

$$T \int_{l} \frac{\partial u}{\partial n} \, ds = T \int \int_{\sigma} \left( \frac{\partial^2 u}{\partial x^2} + \frac{\partial^2 u}{\partial y^2} \right) dx \, dy. \tag{2.2}$$

We shall suppose further that an external force $p(x, y, t)$ per unit area acts on the membrane in the direction of the $u$-axis. The total force acting on the area $\sigma'$ will then be given by

$$\int \int_{\sigma} p(x, y, t) \, dx \, dy. \tag{2.3}$$

The forces given by (2.2) and (2.3) must at all times $t$ be equal and opposite to the inertial force

$$- \int \int_{\sigma} \rho(x, y) \frac{\partial^2 u}{\partial t^2} \, dx \, dy,$$

where $\rho(x, y)$ is the surface density of the membrane.
We thus have the following equation

$$\int \int_{\sigma} \left[ \rho(x, y) \frac{\partial^2 u}{\partial t^2} - T \left( \frac{\partial^2 u}{\partial x^2} + \frac{\partial^2 u}{\partial y^2} \right) + p(x, y, t) \right] dx \, dy = 0.$$

and since $\sigma'$ is arbitrary, it follows that

$$\rho(x, y) \frac{\partial^2 u}{\partial t^2} = T \left( \frac{\partial^2 u}{\partial x^2} + \frac{\partial^2 u}{\partial y^2} \right) + p(x, y, t). \tag{2.4}$$

This is in fact the differential equation of transverse oscillations of a membrane.
In the case of a uniform membrane $\rho = $ const and the equation of small oscillations may be written in the form

$$\frac{\partial^2 u}{\partial t^2} = a^2 \left( \frac{\partial^2 u}{\partial x^2} + \frac{\partial^2 u}{\partial y^2} \right) + f(x, y, t), \tag{2.5}$$

where

$$a = \sqrt{\frac{T}{\rho}}, \quad f(x, y, t) = \frac{p(x, y, t)}{\rho}. \tag{2.6}$$

If there are no external forces $p(x, y, t) = 0$ and equation (2.5) yields the equation of free oscillations of a uniform membrane:

$$\frac{\partial^2 u}{\partial t^2} = a^2 \left( \frac{\partial^2 u}{\partial x^2} + \frac{\partial^2 u}{\partial y^2} \right). \tag{2.7}$$

As in the case of the oscillations of a string, equation (2.4) is in itself insufficient to determine the motion of a membrane. It must be supplemented by specifying the displacements and velocities of all points of the membrane at time $t = 0$:

$$u|_{t=0} = \varphi_0(x, y), \quad \frac{\partial u}{\partial t}\bigg|_{t=0} = \varphi_1(x, y). \tag{2.8}$$

Moreover, since the membrane is fixed on a contour $L$, we must have

$$u|_L = 0 \tag{2.9}$$

for any $t \geqslant 0$.

## § 3. Equations of hydrodynamics and the propagation of sound waves

1. In hydrodynamics, a liquid or gas is regarded as a continuous medium.* This means that any small-volume element of the fluid is considered to be large enough to contain a very large number of molecules. Therefore, when we speak of an infinitely small-volume element we shall always mean a volume which is small in comparison with the total volume of the body but large in comparison with the intermolecular distances. Thus, for example, when one speaks in hydrodynamics of the displacement of a particle of the fluid, one is not concerned with the displacement of an individual molecule but with the displacement of a volume element containing a large number of molecules but regarded as a point.

---

* In our subsequent analysis we shall use the word fluid to designate either a liquid or a gas.

Suppose that the fluid moves with a velocity $\boldsymbol{v}(x, y, z, t)$ whose components along the coordinate axes will be denoted by $v_x(x, y, z, t)$, $v_y(x, y, z, t)$ and $v_z(x, y, z, t)$.

We must emphasis that $\boldsymbol{v}(x, y, z, t)$ is the velocity of the fluid at each given point $x, y, z$ at time $t$, i.e. it refers to definite points of space and not to given particles in the liquid which move in that space; this is also the case for thermodynamic quantities.

It the velocity vector $\boldsymbol{v}(x, y, z, t)$ is known, the trajectories of the individual particles of the fluid are determined by the equation

$$\frac{dx}{dt} = v_x(x, y, z, t), \quad \frac{dy}{dt} = v_y(x, y, z, t), \quad \frac{dz}{dt} = v_z(x, y, z, t).$$

so that the accelerations of the particles of the fluid are given by

$$\frac{d^2x}{dt^2} = \frac{\partial v_x}{\partial t} + \frac{\partial v_x}{\partial x}\cdot\frac{dx}{dt} + \frac{\partial v_x}{\partial y}\cdot\frac{dy}{dt} + \frac{\partial v_x}{\partial z}\cdot\frac{dz}{dt} =$$

$$= \frac{\partial v_x}{\partial t} + \frac{\partial v_x}{\partial x} v_x + \frac{\partial v_x}{\partial y} v_y + \frac{\partial v_x}{\partial z} v_z, \tag{3.1}$$

$$\frac{d^2y}{dt^2} = \frac{\partial v_y}{\partial t} + \frac{\partial v_y}{\partial x} v_x + \frac{\partial v_y}{\partial y} v_y + \frac{\partial v_y}{\partial z} v_z,$$

$$\frac{d^2z}{dt^2} = \frac{\partial v_z}{\partial t} + \frac{\partial v_z}{\partial x} v_x + \frac{\partial v_z}{\partial y} v_y + \frac{\partial v_z}{\partial z} v_z.$$

At each time $t$ and each point $x, y, z$ the fluid is in a state of thermodynamic equilibrium which is determined by the pressure $p(x, y, z, t)$, density $\rho(x, y, z, t)$, temperature $T(x, y, z, t)$, entropy $S(x, y, z, t)$, and internal energy $E(x, y, z, t)$. It is known from thermodynamics that for each medium there are only two independent parameters among the five quantities $p, \rho, T, S$, and $E$. The quantities $p, T$, and $E$ may be regarded as functions of $\rho$ and $S$.

We shall begin the derivation of the hydrodynamic equations with the derivation of an equation representing the conservation of matter in hydrodynamics. Consider a volume $V$ of a fluid bounded by a surface $S$. If there are no sources or sinks inside $V$ then the rate of change of the mass of the fluid in $V$ is equal to the flux of the fluid through the surface $S$. Symbolically this may be written in the form

$$\frac{\partial}{\partial t} \iiint_V \rho \, dV = - \iint_S \rho v_n \, dS,$$

where $v_n$ is the component of $\boldsymbol{v}(x, y, z, t)$ in the direction of the outward normal $n$ of the surface $S$. If we transform the right-hand side by the Gauss' theorem formula and differentiate with respect to $t$ under the integral sign on the left-hand side, we obtain

$$\iiint_V \frac{\partial \rho}{\partial t} \, dV = - \iiint_V \operatorname{div} \rho \boldsymbol{v} \, dV$$

or

$$\iiint_V \left( \frac{\partial \rho}{\partial t} + \operatorname{div} \rho \boldsymbol{v} \right) dV = 0,$$

where

$$\operatorname{div} \rho \boldsymbol{v} = \frac{\partial(\rho v_x)}{\partial x} + \frac{\partial(\rho v_y)}{\partial y} + \frac{\partial(\rho v_z)}{\partial z}.$$

Since the above equation is valid for an arbitrary volume $V$, it follows that

$$\frac{\partial \rho}{\partial t} + \operatorname{div} \rho \boldsymbol{v} = 0. \tag{3.2}$$

This is the so-called *equation of continuity*.

We must now consider the derivation of the equation of motion of an ideal fluid.

An *ideal fluid* will be defined as a deformable continuous medium – moving or at rest – in which the internal forces can be reduced to a normal pressure, so that if we isolate in this fluid a volume $V$ bounded by a surface $S$ then the effect of the remainder of the fluid on this region can be replaced by forces acting at each point of $S$ in the direction of the inward normal. Let this force per unit area, i.e. pressure, be denoted by $p(x, y, z, t)$.

Thus, the resultant of the pressure forces applied to the surface $S$ is equal to

$$- \iint_S p \boldsymbol{n} \, dS,$$

where $n$ is a unit vector in the direction of the outward normal to the surface $S$. From the divergence formula we have

$$- \iint_S p n \, dS = - \iiint_V \operatorname{grad} p \, dV.$$

Moreover, suppose that an external force $F(F_x, F_y, F_z)$ acts per unit mass of the fluid, so that the resultant of such forces acting on the volume $V$ is equal to

$$\iiint_V \rho F \, dV.$$

Finally, the resultant of inertial forces acting on $V$ is

$$- \iiint_V \rho \frac{dv}{dt} \, dV,$$

where $dv/dt$ is the acceleration of the particle of the fluid. The derivative $dv/dt$ denotes not the rate of change of the velocity of the fluid at a given fixed point of space, but the rate of change in the velocity of a particle of the fluid moving in space. This is emphasised by using the symbol $d/dt$ instead of $\partial/\partial t$.

D'Alambert's principle then yields

$$\iiint_V \left( \rho F - \rho \frac{dv}{dt} - \operatorname{grad} p \right) dV = 0.$$

and since $V$ is arbitrary it follows that

$$\frac{dv}{dt} = F - \frac{1}{\rho} \operatorname{grad} p. \tag{3.3}$$

In view of equation (3.1) this may be written in the scalar form

$$\frac{\partial v_x}{\partial t} + \frac{\partial v_x}{\partial x} v_x + \frac{\partial v_x}{\partial y} v_y + \frac{\partial v_x}{\partial z} v_z = F_x - \frac{1}{\rho} \frac{\partial p}{\partial x},$$

$$\frac{\partial v_y}{\partial t} + \frac{\partial v_y}{\partial y} v_x + \frac{\partial v_y}{\partial x} v_y + \frac{\partial v_y}{\partial z} v_z = F_y - \frac{1}{\rho} \frac{\partial p}{\partial y}, \tag{3.3'}$$

$$\frac{\partial v_z}{\partial t} + \frac{\partial v_z}{\partial x} v_x + \frac{\partial v_z}{\partial y} v_y + \frac{\partial v_z}{\partial z} v_z = F_z - \frac{1}{\rho} \frac{\partial p}{\partial z}.$$

These are the equations of motion of an ideal fluid in the form given by Euler.

We thus have the four equations given by (3.2) and (3.3') for the five unknown functions $v_x$, $v_y$, $v_z$, $\rho$, and $p$. In order to obtain one further equation we shall suppose that the motion of the fluid is *adiabatic*, so that the entropy of each particle of the fluid remains constant (although the entropy may vary from point to point) as the matter moves through space, i.e. $dS/dt = 0$ where the total derivative with respect to time represents, as in (3.3), the rate of change in entropy of a given particle of the fluid moving through space. This derivative can also be written in the form

$$\frac{\partial S}{\partial t} + \frac{\partial S}{\partial x} v_x + \frac{\partial S}{\partial y} v_y + \frac{\partial S}{\partial z} v_z = 0.$$

This equation represents the fact that the motion of the ideal fluid is adiabatic. It may happen that at $t = 0$ the entropy is the same at all points of the fluid, and if this is so it will remain constant and equal to the initial value throughout the subsequent motion of the fluid. The above equation can then be written simply as

$$S = S_0 = \text{const.}$$

This type of motion is known as *isentropic*. The pressure $p$ is then given by

$$p = f(\rho, S_0) = f(\rho). \tag{3.4}$$

We thus have five equations: the equation of continuity (3.2), the three equations of motion of an ideal fluid (3.3'), and equation (3.4). They contain the five unknown functions $v_x$, $v_y$, $v_z$, $\rho$, and $p$.

2. The oscillatory motion with small amplitude of a compressible liquid or gas is called a sound wave. At each point of the medium traversed by a sound wave there are alternate compressions and rarefactions. Since the oscillations in the sound wave are small, the velocity $v$ of the wave is also small, so that in Euler's equations (3.3') we can neglect the terms $(\partial v/\partial x)v_x$, .... Similarly, the relative changes in the density and pressure are also small. Let

$$p = p_0 + \bar{p}, \quad \rho = \rho_0 + \bar{\rho}, \tag{3.5}$$

where $\rho_0$, $p_0$ are the equilibrium values of the density and pressure, and $\bar{\rho}$, $\bar{p}$ are the changes in them due to the passage of a sound wave ($\bar{\rho} \ll \rho_0$, $\bar{p} \ll p_0$).

When (3.5) is substituted into the equation of continuity (3.2) and small quantities of the second order are neglected ($\bar{\rho}$, $\bar{p}$, $v$, $\partial v_x/\partial x$, $\partial\bar{\rho}/\partial x$, $\partial\bar{p}/\partial x$, ..., etc. must be regarded as small quantities of the first order) we obtain

$$\frac{\partial\bar{\rho}}{\partial t} + \rho_0 \operatorname{div} v = 0$$

or

$$\frac{\partial s}{\partial t} + \operatorname{div} v = 0. \tag{3.6}$$

where

$$s = \frac{\bar{\rho}}{\rho_0} = \frac{\rho - \rho_0}{\rho_0}.$$

If there are no external forces Euler's equations (3.3′) will on this approximation reduce to

$$\frac{\partial v_x}{\partial t} = -\frac{1}{\rho_0}\frac{\partial\bar{p}}{\partial x}, \quad \frac{\partial v_y}{\partial t} = -\frac{1}{\rho_0}\frac{\partial\bar{p}}{\partial y}, \quad \frac{\partial v_z}{\partial t} = -\frac{1}{\rho_0}\frac{\partial\bar{p}}{\partial z}$$

or in vector form

$$\frac{\partial v}{\partial t} = -\frac{1}{\rho_0}\operatorname{grad}\bar{p}. \tag{3.7}$$

Equations (3.6) and (3.7) contain the unknown functions $v$, $s$, and $\bar{p}$. In order to eliminate one of them, let us return to (3.4), which on our present approximation may be written in the form

$$\bar{p} = f'(\rho_0)\bar{\rho}' = \rho_0 f'(\rho_0)s. \tag{3.8}$$

Substituting (3.8) into equation (3.7), we obtain

$$\frac{\partial v}{\partial t} + a^2\operatorname{grad} s = 0, \tag{3.9}$$

where $a^2 = f'(\rho_0)$, since for all liquids and gases encountered in nature the pressure increases with density at constant entropy, i.e. $f'(\rho) > 0$.

If we take the divergence of (3.9) and interchange the divergence operator with differentiation with respect to time, we obtain

$$\frac{\partial}{\partial t}\operatorname{div} v = -a^2\operatorname{div}\operatorname{grad} s = -a^2\Delta s, \tag{3.10}$$

where

$$\Delta s = \frac{\partial^2 s}{\partial x^2} + \frac{\partial^2 s}{\partial y^2} + \frac{\partial^2 s}{\partial z^2}.$$

Finally, in view of equation (3.6), we obtain

$$\frac{\partial^2 s}{\partial t^2} = a^2 \left( \frac{\partial^2 s}{\partial x^2} + \frac{\partial^2 s}{\partial y^2} + \frac{\partial^2 s}{\partial z^2} \right). \tag{3.11}$$

A wave equation of the form given by (3.11) can also be obtained for the pressure $\tilde{p}$ and for the velocity $\boldsymbol{v}$.

Let us suppose that at the initial time $t = 0$ the velocity potential was $u_0(x, y, z)$, i.e.

$$\boldsymbol{v}|_{t=0} = - \operatorname{grad} u_0(x, y, z). \tag{3.12}$$

From equation (3.10) we have

$$\boldsymbol{v}(x, y, z, t) = \boldsymbol{v}|_{t=0} - a^2 \operatorname{grad} \int_0^t s \, dt$$

or, in view of (3.12),

$$\boldsymbol{v} = - \operatorname{grad}[u_0(x, y, z) + a^2 \int_0^t s \, dt] = - \operatorname{grad} u(x, y, z, t), \tag{3.13}$$

which means that we can define a velocity potential $u(x, y, z, t)$ at any time $t$:

$$u(x, y, z, t) = u_0(x, y, z) + a^2 \int_0^t s \, dt. \tag{3.14}$$

We shall show that the velocity potential $u(x, y, z, t)$ satisfies the wave equation. In point of fact, by differentiating (3.14) twice with respect to $t$, we obtain

$$\frac{\partial^2 u}{\partial t^2} = a^2 \frac{\partial s}{\partial t}. \tag{3.15}$$

On the other hand, by substituting (3.13) into (3.6) we have

$$\frac{\partial s}{\partial t} = \operatorname{div} \operatorname{grad} u = \Delta u. \tag{3.16}$$

Comparison of (3.15) and (3.16) finally yields

$$\frac{\partial^2 u}{\partial t^2} = a^2 \left( \frac{\partial^2 u}{\partial x^2} + \frac{\partial^2 u}{\partial y^2} + \frac{\partial^2 u}{\partial z^2} \right). \tag{3.17}$$

We know that a knowledge of the velocity potential $u(x, y, z, t)$ is sufficient for the determination of the entire motion of a liquid or gas, since

$$\boldsymbol{v} = - \operatorname{grad} u, \quad s = \frac{1}{a^2} \frac{\partial u}{\partial t}, \quad \bar{p} = \rho_0 \frac{\partial u}{\partial t}. \tag{3.18}$$

In order to formulate the initial boundary conditions let us suppose that the liquid or gas occupies a volume $V$ bounded by a surface $\sigma$. The relative change $s$ in the density of the gas and the velocity $\boldsymbol{v}$ at each point in $V$ are given at $t = 0$, i.e. we have the initial conditions in the form

$$u|_{t=0} = \varphi_0(x, y, z), \quad \frac{\partial u}{\partial t}\bigg|_{t=0} = a^2 s = \varphi_1(x, y, z).$$

If the surface $\sigma$ is an impenetrable wall, the normal component of the velocity is zero, and this yields the boundary condition

$$\frac{\partial u}{\partial n}\bigg|_{\Sigma} = 0.$$

## § 4. Heat transfer equation for an isotropic solid

Consider a solid whose temperature at the point $x, y, z$ at time $t$ is given by the function $u(x, y, z, t)$. If different parts of the body are at different temperatures, there will be a transfer of heat between them. Consider a small element $\Delta S$ of a surface $S$ drawn inside the body. It is assumed in the theory of heat transfer that the amount of heat $\Delta Q$ passing through the element $\Delta S$ in a time $\Delta t$ is proportional to $\Delta t$, $\Delta S$ and to the normal derivative $\partial u/\partial n$, i.e.

$$\Delta Q = - k \frac{\partial u}{\partial n} \Delta S \cdot \Delta t = - k \Delta S \cdot \Delta t \operatorname{grad}_n u, \tag{4.1}$$

Where $k > 0$ is the thermal conductivity and $n$ is the normal to the surface element $\Delta S$ in the direction of heat transfer. We shall suppose that the body is isotropic as far as heat transfer is concerned, i.e. the thermal conductivity $k$ depends only on the coordinates $x, y, z$ of points in the body but is independent of the direction of the normal to the surface $S$ at each point.

Let $q$ be the *heat flux*, i.e. the amount of heat passing through the unit surface area per unit time. Equation (4.1) can then be written in the form

$$q = -k \frac{\partial u}{\partial n}. \tag{4.2}$$

To derive the heat-transfer equation, consider an arbitrary volume $V$ bounded by a smooth closed surface $S$. It is readily seen that the amount of heat entering through the surface $S$ in a time interval $t_1, t_2$ is, in view of (4.1), given by

$$Q_1 = -\int_{t_1}^{t_2} dt \iint_S k(x, y, z) \frac{\partial u}{\partial n} dS,$$

where $n$ is the inward normal to the surface $S$.

Consider a volume element $\Delta V$. To change the temperature of this volume by $\Delta u$ in a time $\Delta t$, we must introduce an amount of heat

$$\Delta Q_2 = [u(x, y, z, t+\Delta t) - u(x, y, z, t)]\gamma(x, y, z)\rho(x, y, z)\Delta V,$$

where $\rho(x, y, z)$ and $\gamma(x, y, z)$ are respectively the density and the specific heat of the medium. It follows that the amount of heat which is necessary to change the temperature of the medium in $V$ by $\Delta u = u(x, y, z, t_2) - u(x, y, z, t_1)$ is

$$Q_2 = \iiint_V [u(x, y, z, t_2) - u(x, y, z, t_1)]\gamma\rho dV$$

where

$$Q_2 = \int_{t_1}^{t_2} dt \iiint_V \gamma\rho \frac{\partial u}{\partial t} dV,$$

since

$$u(x, y, z, t_2) - u(x, y, z, t_1) = \int_{t_1}^{t_2} \frac{\partial u}{\partial t} dt.$$

We shall suppose that the body under consideration contains heat sources, and let $F(x, y, z, t)$ be the density of the heat sources, i.e. the amount of absorbed or liberated heat per unit volume per unit time. The amount of heat liberated or absorbed in $V$ in the time intervals $t_1$, $t_2$ will then be

$$Q_3 = \int_{t_1}^{t_2} dt \iiint_V F(x, y, z, t)\, dV.$$

It is evident that $Q_2 = Q_1 + Q_3$, i.e.

$$\int_{t_1}^{t_2} dt \iiint_V \gamma\rho \frac{\partial u}{\partial t}\, dV =$$

$$= - \int_{t_1}^{t_2} dt \iint_S k \frac{\partial u}{\partial n}\, dS + \int_{t_1}^{t_2} dt \iiint_V F(x, y, z, t)\, dV,$$

or using the divergence formula in the second integral we have

$$\int_{t_1}^{t_2} dt \iiint_V \left[ \gamma\rho \frac{\partial u}{\partial t} - \operatorname{div}(k\operatorname{grad} u) - F(x, y, z, t) \right] dV = 0.$$

Since the integrand is continuous, and $V$ and the time interval ($t_1$ and $t_2$) are arbitrary, it follows that for any point $x, y, z$ in the body under consideration, and for any time $t$, we must have

$$\gamma\rho \frac{\partial u}{\partial t} = \operatorname{div}(k\operatorname{grad} u) + F(x, y, z, t) \qquad (4.3)$$

or

$$\gamma\rho \frac{\partial u}{\partial t} = \frac{\partial}{\partial x}\left( k \frac{\partial u}{\partial x} \right) + \frac{\partial}{\partial y}\left( k \frac{\partial u}{\partial y} \right) +$$

$$+ \frac{\partial}{\partial z}\left( k \frac{\partial u}{\partial z} \right) + F(x, y, z, t). \qquad (4.3')$$

This is the *heat transfer equation for a uniform isotropic body.*
If the body is uniform, $\gamma$, $\rho$, and $k$ are constant and equation (4.3')

may be written in the form

$$\frac{\partial u}{\partial t} = a^2 \left( \frac{\partial^2 u}{\partial x^2} + \frac{\partial^2 u}{\partial y^2} + \frac{\partial^2 u}{\partial z^2} \right) + f(x, y, z, t), \qquad (4.4)$$

where

$$a = \sqrt{\frac{k}{\gamma\rho}}, \quad f(x, y, z, t) = \frac{F(x, y, z, t)}{\gamma\rho}.$$

If there are no sources of heat in the uniform body under consideration, i.e. if $F(x, y, z, t) \equiv 0$, we obtain the homogeneous heat-transfer equation

$$\frac{\partial u}{\partial t} = a^2 \left( \frac{\partial^2 u}{\partial x^2} + \frac{\partial^2 u}{\partial y^2} + \frac{\partial^2 u}{\partial z^2} \right). \qquad (4.5)$$

In the special case when the temperature is a function of $x$, $y$, and $t$ only, for example in a very thin uniform plate, equation (4.5) becomes

$$\frac{\partial u}{\partial t} = a^2 \left( \frac{\partial^2 u}{\partial x^2} + \frac{\partial^2 u}{\partial y^2} \right). \qquad (4.6)$$

Finally, for a one-dimensional body, for example a uniform rod, the heat-transfer equation becomes

$$\frac{\partial u}{\partial t} = a^2 \frac{\partial^2 u}{\partial x^2}. \qquad (4.7)$$

We note that in deriving equations (4.6) and (4.7) we did not take into account heat transfer between the surface of the plate or rod and the surrounding space.

Equation (4.3) is not in itself sufficient to determine the temperature distribution inside the body at any time $t$. It must be supplemented by the temperature distribution at $t = 0$ (initial condition) and the thermal conditions on the surface $S$ of the body (boundary conditions).

The boundary condition may be formulated in a number of ways

1. the temperature is specified at each point on $S$:

$$u|_S = \Psi_1(P, t), \qquad (4.8)$$

where $\Psi_1(P, t)$ is a given function of position on $S$ and of time $t \geqslant 0$.

2. The heat flux

$$q = - k \frac{\partial u}{\partial n},$$

is prescribed on the surface $S$, i.e.

$$\frac{\partial u}{\partial n}\bigg|_S = \Psi_2(P, t), \tag{4.9}$$

where $\Psi_2(P, t)$ is a given function which can be expressed in terms of the heat flux:

$$\Psi_2(P, t) = - \frac{q(P, t)}{k}.$$

3. Heat-transfer occurs between the surface of the solid and the surrounding medium, whose temperature $u_0$ is given. The law of heat-transfer is usually very complicated, but in order to simplify the analysis we shall assume that Newton's law applies. This law states that the amount of heat transferred per unit time from a unit area on the surface of the body to the surrounding medium is proportional to the difference between the temperatures of the surface and of the surrounding medium:

$$q = H(u - u_0),$$

where $H$ is the heat-transfer coefficient. In general, this coefficient is a function of the temperature difference $u - u_0$ and depends on the nature of the surface and of the surrounding medium (it may vary over the surface of the body). We shall, however, suppose that $H$ is constant over the surface of the body and is independent of temperature.

In view of the law of conservation of energy, we must satisfy the following boundary conditions on the surface $S$:

$$H(u - u_0) = - k \frac{\partial u}{\partial n},$$

where $n$ is the outward normal to the surface $S$, or if we substitute

$h = H/u$

$$\frac{\partial u}{\partial n} + h(u - u_0)\Big|_S = 0. \tag{4.10}$$

It follows that the problem of the propagation of heat in an isotropic solid may be formulated as follows.

*It is necessary to find the solution of the heat-transfer equation* (4.3) *which satisfies the initial condition*

$$u|_{t=0} = \varphi(x, y, z)$$

*and one of the boundary conditions* (4.8), (4.9), *or* (4.10).

### § 5. Problems which may be reduced to the Laplace equation

**1. Steady state temperature distribution in a uniform solid.** It was shown in the preceding section that the heat-transfer equation for an isotropic uniform body in the absence of heat sources is

$$\frac{\partial u}{\partial t} = a^2 \left( \frac{\partial^2 u}{\partial x^2} + \frac{\partial^2 u}{\partial y^2} + \frac{\partial^2 u}{\partial z^2} \right). \tag{5.1}$$

Let us suppose now that the temperature distribution throughout the body has reached a steady state, i.e. it is independent of time. This means that $\partial u/\partial t = 0$ and equation (5.1) becomes

$$\frac{\partial^2 u}{\partial x^2} + \frac{\partial^2 u}{\partial y^2} + \frac{\partial^2 u}{\partial z^2} = 0. \tag{5.2}$$

We thus see that the Laplace equation (5.2) is satisfied by the temperature function $u(x, y, z)$ describing the steady state temperature distribution in a uniform body. To determine $u(x, y, z)$ we need no longer satisfy the initial temperature distribution (initial condition): it is sufficient to prescribe one time-independent boundary condition. The determination of the solution of equation (5.2) from the values of $u$ on the boundary of the region under consideration is referred to as Dirichlet's problem.

The determination of the solution of equation (5.2), subject to the boundary condition $(\partial u/\partial n_S = \varphi(P)$ is referred to as Neumann's problem.

**2. Potential motion of incompressible fluid.** Consider the steady state motion of an incompressible fluid. Suppose that the motion of the fluid is irrotational, i.e. the velocity $v(x, y, z)$ can be expressed as the gradient of a scalar function (potential):

$$v = - \operatorname{grad} \varphi. \tag{5.3}$$

The density $\rho$ of an incompressible fluid is constant, and it follows from the continuity equation (4.1) that

$$\operatorname{div} v = 0. \tag{5.4}$$

Substituting (5.3) into (5.4), we obtain

$$\operatorname{div} \operatorname{grad} \varphi = 0 \quad \text{or} \quad \frac{\partial^2 \varphi}{\partial x^2} + \frac{\partial^2 \varphi}{\partial y^2} + \frac{\partial^2 \varphi}{\partial z^2} = 0, \tag{5.5}$$

i.e. the velocity potential $\varphi$ satisfies the Laplace equation (5.5).

We have seen in the preceding sections that problems in mathematical physics can be reduced to the solution of partial differential equations, subject to certain additional conditions. The latter frequently take the form of boundary conditions, i.e. conditions specified on the boundary of the medium under consideration, and initial conditions referring to the particular time at which the study of the particular physical phenomenon begins.

The solutions obtained from the equations of mathematical physics provide a mathematical description of physical phenomena represented by these equations. Since in setting up models of physical phenomena with the aid of the equations of mathematical physics we are always forced to abstract and approximate, the final results obtained from such analyses are never physically exact.

It follows that any problem in mathematical physics which has been correctly formulated should satisfy the following three requirements: (1) it should admit of a solution; (2) the solution should be unique; and (3) the solution should be stable, i.e. a small change in any of the basic data for the problem should give rise to a correspondingly small change in the solution. The requirement of existence and uniqueness ensures that the basic data of the problem are internally consistent and are sufficient for a unique solution. The requirement of stability is necessary for the following reason: the data of any concrete physical problem, particularly if they are experimental data, are always subject to an uncertainty, so that it is essential for a small error in these data to lead to a small uncertainty in the solution. This requirement ensures that the problem is physically determinate.

**Problems.** (1) A thin uniform cylindrical rod executes longitudinal oscillations in which its transverse cross-sections are displaced along the $x$-axis without change of form. Show that the equation for small oscillations of the rod is

$$\frac{\partial^2 u}{\partial t^2} = a^2 \frac{\partial^2 u}{\partial x^2}, \quad a^2 = \frac{E}{\rho},$$

where $u(x, t)$ is the displacement of a cross-section at a point $x$ at time $t$, $\rho$ is the volume density, and $E$ is Young's modulus.

(2) A heavy uniform flexible string of length $l$ is suspended vertically from one of its ends $(x = l)$. Show that the equation for small oscillations of the string under the action of gravitational forces is

$$\frac{\partial}{\partial x}\left( x \frac{\partial u}{\partial x} \right) = \frac{1}{a^2} \frac{\partial^2 u}{\partial t^2}, \quad a = \sqrt{g},$$

where $u(x, t)$ is the displacement from the position of equilibrium at time $t$ and $g$ is the gravitational acceleration.

(3) Derive the equation for the transfer of heat in a uniform ring of very small transverse cross-section with allowance for heat-transfer to the surrounding medium.
*Answer*:

$$\frac{\partial u}{\partial t} = a^2 \frac{\partial^2 u}{\partial \theta^2} - b(u - u_0), \quad a = \sqrt{\frac{k}{c\rho}}, \quad b = \frac{hp}{\sigma k},$$

where $\theta$ is the length of an arc of the ring, $k$ and $h$ are the internal and external heat-transfer coefficients, $c$ is the specific heat, $\rho$ is the density, $\sigma$ is the area, $p$ is the perimeter of the transverse cross-sections, and $u_0$ is the temperature of the surrounding medium.

Chapter 2

# CLASSIFICATION OF SECOND ORDER EQUATIONS

## § 6. Types of second order equations

Consider the second order equation

$$\sum_{i,j=1}^{n} a_{ij}(x_1, \ldots, x_n) \frac{\partial^2 u}{\partial x_i \partial x_j} +$$

$$+ f\left(x_1, \ldots, x_n, u, \frac{\partial u}{\partial x_1}, \ldots, \frac{\partial u}{\partial x_n}\right) = 0. \tag{6.1}$$

where the coefficients $a_{ij}$ are given functions in a domain $D$ of the space $(x_1, \ldots, x_n)$, and $a_{ij} = a_{ji}$. All functions and independent variables will be taken to be real.

Equations of the form given by (6.1) may be classified at a point as follows. Let us consider a particular point $(x_1^0, \ldots, x_n^0)$ in the domain $D$ and construct the quadratic form

$$\sum_{i,j=1}^{n} a_{ij}(x_1^0, \ldots, x_n^0) t_i t_j. \tag{6.2}$$

Equation (6.1) is of the *elliptic type* at the point $(x_1^0, \ldots, x_n^0)$ if at this point the quadratic form given by (6.2) is non-singular and definite, i.e. it can be reduced by a real linear transformation to a sum of $n$ squares all of the same sign.

Equation (6.1) is of the *hyperbolic type* at the point $x_1^0, \ldots, x_n^0)$ (if at this point the quadratic form given by (6.2) is non-singular and indefinite, i.e. it can be reduced by a real linear transformation to the sum of $n$ squares, not all of the same sign.

Equation (6.1) is of the *ultra-hyperbolic type* at the point $(x_1^0, \ldots, x_n^0)$ if at this point the quadratic form given by (6.2) can be reduced to the sum of $n$ squares with more than one coefficient of either sign, all coefficients being non-zero.

Equation (6.1) is of the *parabolic type* at the point $(x_1^0, \ldots, x_n^0)$ if at this point the quadratic form given by (6.2) is singular, i.e. it can be reduced by a real linear transformation to the sum of fewer than $n$ squares, not necessarily all of the same sign.

Equation (6.1) is of the *elliptic type,* the hyperbolic type, and so on in the domain $D$ if at all points of this region it is respectively of the elliptic type, hyperbolic type, and so on.

If the coefficients $a_{ij}$ are constant, the membership of the equation of any particular type is independent of the values of the independent variables. The simplest equation of the elliptic type is the Laplace equation; the wave equation is an example of the hyperbolic type, and finally, the heat-transfer equation is of the parabolic type.

## § 7. Reduction of second order equations with constant coefficients to the canonical form

Consider the following partial differential equation with constant coefficients

$$\sum_{i,j=1}^{n} a_{ij} \frac{\partial^2 u}{\partial x_i \partial x_j} + \sum_{i=1}^{n} b_i \frac{\partial u}{\partial x_i} + cu = f(x_1, \ldots, x_n). \qquad (7.1)$$

Let us replace $(x_1, \ldots, x_n)$ by new independent variables $(\xi_1, \xi_n)$ with the aid of the linear transformation

$$\xi_k = \sum_{i=1}^{n} c_{ki} x_i \qquad (k = 1, 2, \ldots, n). \qquad (7.2)$$

We shall assume that this transformation is non-singular, i.e. the determinant $|c_{ki}|$ is not equal to zero. Derivatives with respect to the old variables can be expressed in terms of derivatives with respect to the new variables as follows:

$$\frac{\partial u}{\partial x_i} = \sum_{k=1}^{n} c_{ki} \frac{\partial u}{\partial \xi_k}, \quad \frac{\partial^2 u}{\partial x_i \partial x_j} = \sum_{k,l=1}^{n} c_{ki} c_{lj} \frac{\partial^2 u}{\partial \xi_k \partial \xi_l}. \qquad (7.3)$$

Substituting (7.3) into (7.1) we obtain

$$\sum_{k,l=1}^{n} \bar{a}_{kl} \frac{\partial^2 u}{\partial \xi_k \partial \xi_l} + \sum_{i=1}^{n} \bar{b}_i \frac{\partial u}{\partial \xi_i} + cu = f_1(\xi_1, \ldots, \xi_n), \qquad (7.4)$$

where

$$\bar{a}_{kl} = \sum_{i,j=1}^{n} a_{ij} c_{ki} c_{lj}. \tag{7.5}$$

It can readily be verified that the transformation formulae given by (7.5) for the coefficients of the second order derivatives of $u$ are identical with the transformation formulae for the coefficients of the quadratic form

$$\sum_{i,j=1}^{n} a_{ij} t_i t_j, \tag{7.6}$$

when the independent variables are transformed in accordance with (7.2), and (7.6) is subjected to the linear transformation

$$t_i = \sum_{k=1}^{n} c_{ki} \tau_k, \tag{7.7}$$

which reduces it to the form

$$\sum_{k,l=1}^{n} \bar{a}_{kl} \tau_k \tau_l. \tag{7.8}$$

It is shown in algebra that it is always possible to choose the coefficients $c_{ik}$ so that the quadratic form (7.6) can be written as the sum of squares, i.e.*

$$\sum_{k=1}^{n} \lambda_k \tau_k^2, \tag{7.8'}$$

or, in other words, $a_{kl} = 0$, when $k \neq l$ and $\bar{a}_{kk} = \lambda_k$. The coefficients $\lambda_k$ are equal to $\pm 1$ or zero respectively. The signs of $\lambda_k$ determine the type of equation (7.1). The transformed equation (7.4) is of the form

$$\sum_{k=1}^{n} \lambda_k \frac{\partial^2 u}{\partial \xi_k^2} + \sum_{i=1}^{n} \bar{b}_i \frac{\partial u}{\partial \xi_i} + cu = f_1(\xi_1, \ldots, \xi_n). \tag{7.9}$$

which is called its *canonical form*.

---

* It may be shown that for quadratic forms the number of positive and negative $\lambda_k$ is invariant under a linear transformation which reduces (7.6) to (7.8').

Let us suppose that all the $\lambda_k$ are non-zero, i.e. equation (7.1) is not of the parabolic type. We shall show that in this case we can remove all first-order derivatives by transforming the function $u$. If we substitute

$$u = v e^{-\frac{1}{2}\sum_{k=1}^{n}(\bar{b}_k/\lambda_k)\xi_k}.$$

into (7.1) we obtain

$$\sum_{k=1}^{n} \lambda_k \frac{\partial^2 v}{\partial \xi_k^2} + c_1 v = f_2(\xi_1, \ldots, \xi_n).$$

For an equation of the elliptic type $\lambda_k = 1$ or $-1$, and on multiplying (if necessary) both sides of the equation by $-1$, we may suppose that all the $\lambda_k$ are equal to 1. Therefore, using the same notation as before, we may conclude that any linear equation of the elliptic type with constant coefficients may be reduced to the form

$$\sum_{k=1}^{n} \frac{\partial^2 u}{\partial x_k^2} + c_1 u = f_2(x_1, \ldots, x_n). \tag{7.10}$$

In the case of the hyperbolic type, we may suppose that there are $n + 1$ independent variables and let $\xi_{n+1} = t$. Any linear equation of the hyperbolic type with constant coefficients can then be reduced to the form

$$\frac{\partial^2 u}{\partial t^2} - \sum_{k=1}^{n} \frac{\partial^2 u}{\partial x_k^2} + c_1 u = f_3(x_1, \ldots, x_n, t). \tag{7.11}$$

In the case of equation (6.1) with variable coefficients, it is possible to find for each point $(x_1^0, \ldots, x_n^0)$ in a domain $D$ a non-singular transformation of the independent variables which will reduce (6.1) to the canonical form at that point. For each point $(x_1^0, \ldots, x_n^0)$ it is possible, in general, to find a particular transformation for the independent variables which will reduce equation (6.1) to the canonical form; at other points, this transformation may not reduce the equation to the canonical form. If we exclude the case of constant coefficients, a differential equation with more than two independent variables cannot, in general, be reduced to a canonical form by means of a transformation of the independent variables, even in a domain which is as small as desired. In the case of two independent variables, on the other hand, a transformation of this kind does exist under very general assumptions about the coefficients of (6.1). This will be proved in the following section.

## § 8. Reduction of second order equations with two independent variables to the canonical form

Consider the quasi-linear second-order equation with two independent variables

$$A \frac{\partial^2 u}{\partial x^2} + 2B \frac{\partial^2 u}{\partial x \partial y} + C \frac{\partial^2 u}{\partial y^2} + F\left(x, y, z, \frac{\partial u}{\partial x}, \frac{\partial u}{\partial y}\right) = 0, \quad (8.1)$$

where the coefficients $A$, $B$ and $C$ are functions of $x$ and $y$ and have continuous first and second-order derivatives. We shall suppose that $A$, $B$ and $C$ do not vanish at the same time.
The quadratic form corresponding to (8.1) is

$$A t_1^2 + 2B t_1 t_2 + C t_2^2. \qquad (8.2)$$

The differential equation given by (8.1) is
(1) of the hyperbolic type if $B^2 - AC > 0$;
(2) of the parabolic type if $B^2 - AC = 0$; and
(3) of the elliptic type if $B^2 - AC < 0$.
Let us transform the independent variables by substituting

$$\xi = \xi(x, y), \quad \eta = \eta(x, y). \qquad (8.3)$$

The functions $\xi$ and $\eta$ are continuously differentiable and the Jacobian is such that in the domain $D$

$$\frac{D(\xi, \eta)}{D(x, y)} = \begin{vmatrix} \dfrac{\partial \xi}{\partial x}, & \dfrac{\partial \xi}{\partial y} \\[2mm] \dfrac{\partial \eta}{\partial x}, & \dfrac{\partial \eta}{\partial y} \end{vmatrix} \neq 0 \qquad (8.4)$$

In terms of the new independent variables $\xi$ and $\eta$, equation (8.1) may be written in the form

$$\bar{A} \frac{\partial^2 u}{\partial \xi^2} + 2\bar{B} \frac{\partial^2 u}{\partial \xi \partial \eta} + \bar{C} \frac{\partial^2 u}{\partial \eta^2} + \bar{F} \left( \xi, \eta, u, \frac{\partial u}{\partial \xi}, \frac{\partial u}{\partial \eta} \right) = 0, \quad (8.5)$$

where

$$\bar{A}(\xi, \eta) = A \left( \frac{\partial \xi}{\partial x} \right)^2 + 2B \frac{\partial \xi}{\partial x} \frac{\partial \xi}{\partial y} + C \left( \frac{\partial \xi}{\partial y} \right)^2,$$

$$\bar{C}(\xi, \eta) = A \left( \frac{\partial \eta}{\partial x} \right)^2 + 2B \frac{\partial \eta}{\partial x} \frac{\partial \eta}{\partial y} + C \left( \frac{\partial \eta}{\partial y} \right)^2, \quad (8.6)$$

$$\bar{B}(\xi, \eta) = A \frac{\partial \xi}{\partial x} \frac{\partial \eta}{\partial x} + B \left( \frac{\partial \xi}{\partial x} \frac{\partial \eta}{\partial y} + \frac{\partial \xi}{\partial y} \frac{\partial \eta}{\partial x} \right) + C \frac{\partial \xi}{\partial y} \frac{\partial \eta}{\partial y}.$$

It can readily be verified by direct substitution that

$$\bar{B}^2 - \bar{A}\bar{C} = (B^2 - AC) \left( \frac{\partial \xi}{\partial x} \frac{\partial \eta}{\partial y} - \frac{\partial \xi}{\partial y} \frac{\partial \eta}{\partial x} \right)^2, \quad (8.7)$$

and hence it is easy to see that the transformation of the independent variables does not modify the type of the equation.

We shall now show that the two functions $\xi$ and $\eta$ can be chosen so that only one of the following conditions is satisfied

1) $\bar{A} = 0$, $\bar{C} = 0$; 2) $\bar{A} = 0$, $\bar{B} = 0$; 3) $\bar{A} = \bar{C}$, $\bar{B} = 0$.

The transformed equation (8.5) will then assume its simplest form.

1. $B^2 - AC > 0$. Equation (8.1) is of the hyperbolic type in the domain $D$ under consideration. We may suppose that at the point $(x_0, y_0)$, in whose neighbourhood we shall reduce (8.1) to the canonical form, either $A \neq 0$ or $C \neq 0$.

Consider the first-order differential equation

$$A \left( \frac{\partial \varphi}{\partial x} \right)^2 + 2B \frac{\partial \varphi}{\partial x} \frac{\partial \varphi}{\partial y} + C \left( \frac{\partial \varphi}{\partial y} \right)^2 = 0. \quad (8.8)$$

and suppose that $A \neq 0$. Since $B^2 - AC > 0$, equation (8.8) may be written in the form

$$\left[ A \frac{\partial \varphi}{\partial x} + (B + \sqrt{B^2 - AC}) \frac{\partial \varphi}{\partial y} \right] \times$$

$$\times \left[ A \frac{\partial \varphi}{\partial x} + (B - \sqrt{B^2 - AC}) \frac{\partial \varphi}{\partial y} \right] = 0.$$

This equation splits into two, i.e.

$$A \frac{\partial \varphi}{\partial x} + (B + \sqrt{B^2 - AC}) \frac{\partial \varphi}{\partial y} = 0, \tag{8.8a}$$

$$A \frac{\partial \varphi}{\partial x} + (B - \sqrt{B^2 - AC}) \frac{\partial \varphi}{\partial y} = 0. \tag{8.8b}$$

Therefore, the solutions of each of the equations given by (8.8a) and (8.8b) will be solutions of equation (8.8).

To integrate equations (8.8a) and (8.8b) let us set up a corresponding ordinary differential equation

$$\frac{dx}{A} = \frac{dy}{B + \sqrt{B^2 - AC}}, \quad \frac{dx}{A} = \frac{dy}{B - \sqrt{B^2 - AC}}$$

or

$$\begin{aligned} A\,dy - (B + \sqrt{B^2 - AC})\,dx &= 0, \\ A\,dy - (B - \sqrt{B^2 - AC})\,dx &= 0. \end{aligned} \tag{8.9}$$

We note that equations (8.9) may be written in the form of the single equation

$$A\,dy^2 - 2B\,dx\,dy + C\,dx^2 = 0. \tag{8.9a}$$

The coefficients of the differential equations (8.9) have continuous first-order and second-order partial derivatives (this follows from our assumptions about the coefficients $A$, $B$, and $C$). Since $A(x_0, y_0) \neq 0$, equations (8.9) have the integrals

$$\varphi_1(x, y) = \text{const}, \quad \varphi_2(x, y) = \text{const} \tag{8.10}$$

and their left-hand sides have continuous first-order and second-order partial derivatives in the neighbourhood of the point $(x_0, y_0)$. The left-hand sides of the solutions given by (8.10) are also the solutions of (8.8a) and (8.8b), and therefore of equation (8.8).

The curves defined by (8.10) are called the *characteristic curves*, or simply the *characteristics* of equation (8.1), while equation (8.8) is the equation of characteristics.

For equations of the hyperbolic type, $B^2 - AC > 0$ and the integrals given by (8.10) are real and different. In this case we have two different families of real characteristics.

Let us substitute

$$\xi = \xi(x, y) = \varphi_1(x, y), \quad \eta = \eta(x, y) = \varphi_2(x, y),$$

into the transformation given by (8.3), where $\varphi_1(x, y)$ and $\varphi_2(x, y)$ respectively are twice continuously differentiable solutions of (8.8a) and (8.8b). These solutions may be chosen so that the Jacobian $D(\varphi_1, \varphi_2)/D(x, y)$ does not vanish in a neighbourhood of the point $(x_0, y_0)$ in the domain $D$. Since $A \neq 0$, it follows from equations (8.8a) and (8.8b) that

$$\begin{vmatrix} \dfrac{\partial \varphi_1}{\partial x} & \dfrac{\partial \varphi_1}{\partial y} \\[2mm] \dfrac{\partial \varphi_2}{\partial x} & \dfrac{\partial \varphi_2}{\partial y} \end{vmatrix} = -\frac{\sqrt{B^2 - AC}}{A} \frac{\partial \varphi_1}{\partial y} \frac{\partial \varphi_2}{\partial y}.$$

Hence, it follows from the fact that $B^2 - AC > 0$ and from equations (8.8a) and (8.8b) that if the Jacobian vanishes at a given point, both first-order partial derivatives of $\varphi_1$ or $\varphi_2$ are zero at this point. We must therefore find those solutions of equations (8.8a) and (8.8b) in which the two first-order partial derivatives are not zero at the same time.*

The functions $\varphi_1(x, y)$ and $\varphi_2(x, y)$ satisfy equations (8.8), and in view of (8.6) we have $\bar{A} = \bar{C} = 0$ in equation (8.5). The coefficient $\bar{B}$ is not equal to zero throughout the domain under consideration, which follows from (8.4) and (8.7). On dividing equation (8.5) by $2\bar{B}$ we reduce it to the form

$$\frac{\partial^2 u}{\partial \xi \partial \eta} = F_1 \left( \xi, \eta, u, \frac{\partial u}{\partial \xi}, \frac{\partial u}{\partial \eta} \right). \tag{8.11}$$

This is also referred to as the canonical form.

When $A = C = 0$, equation (8.1) will also be of the form given by (8.11). By substituting

$$\xi = \alpha + \beta, \quad \eta = \alpha - \beta$$

---

* For this it is sufficient to solve the Cauchy problem for equations (8.8a) and (8.8b) by specifying at $x = x_0$ the values of $\varphi_1(x, y)$ and $\varphi_2(x, y)$, so that $\varphi_{1y}'(x_0, y_0) \neq 0$ and $\varphi_{2y}'(x_0, y_0) \neq 0$.

we shall reduce equation (8.11) to the form

$$\frac{\partial^2 u}{\partial \alpha^2} - \frac{\partial^2 u}{\partial \beta^2} = \Phi\left(\alpha, \beta, u, \frac{\partial u}{\partial \alpha}, \frac{\partial u}{\partial \beta}\right). \tag{8.12}$$

This is the *canonical form of equations of the hyperbolic type.*

2. $B^2 - AC = 0$. In the domain $D$ equation (8.1) is of the parabolic type. Since we are assuming that the coefficients $A$, $B$ and $C$ in (8.1) do not vanish at the same time, it follows from the condition $B^2 - AC = 0$ that at each point in $D$ one of the coefficients $A$, $C$ is not zero. Suppose for example that $A \neq 0$ at $(x_0, y_0)$ in whose neighbourhood we shall reduce equation (8.1) to the canonical form. The two equations (8.8a) and (8.8b) will then be identical and assume the common form

$$A \frac{\partial \varphi}{\partial x} + B \frac{\partial \varphi}{\partial y} = 0. \tag{8.13}$$

It can readily be seen that since $B^2 - AC = 0$, any solution of (8.13) will also satisfy the equation

$$B \frac{\partial \varphi}{\partial x} + C \frac{\partial \varphi}{\partial y} = 0. \tag{8.14}$$

As in the preceding section, we can find a solution $\varphi(x, y)$ of equation (8.13) such that $\varphi(x, y)$ has continuous second-order derivatives, whilst its first order derivatives are not both equal to zero in the vicinity of the point $(x_0, y_0)$. We note that for an equation of the parabolic type we have the single family of real characteristics $\varphi(x, y) = $ const. Let us substitute

$$\xi = \varphi(x, y),$$

in (8.3), where $\varphi(x, y)$ is the solution of (8.13), and let us take $\eta(x, y)$ to be any twice differentiable function, so that the Jacobian $D(\xi, \eta)/D(x, y)$ is not equal to zero in the vicinity of $(x_0, y_0)$. We then have $\bar{A} \equiv 0$ in equation (8.5), which follows from (8.6), whilst the coefficient of $\partial^2 u/\partial \xi \partial \eta$ is of the form

$$\bar{B} = \left(A \frac{\partial \varphi}{\partial x} + B \frac{\partial \varphi}{\partial y}\right) \frac{\partial \eta}{\partial x} + \left(B \frac{\partial \varphi}{\partial x} + C \frac{\partial \varphi}{\partial y}\right) \frac{\partial \eta}{\partial y}.$$

According to (8.13) and (8.14) we have $\bar{B} \equiv 0$ in the vicinity of

$(x_0, y_0)$. The coefficient $\bar{C}$ in (8.5) transforms to

$$\bar{C} = \frac{1}{A}\left(A\,\frac{\partial \eta}{\partial x} + B\,\frac{\partial \eta}{\partial y}\right)^2,$$

and hence $\bar{C} \neq 0$, since otherwise the Jacobian would vanish in view of (8.13). We can then divide (8.5) by $\bar{C} \neq 0$, thereby reducing it to the form

$$\frac{\partial^2 u}{\partial \eta^2} = F_2\left(\xi,\, \eta,\, u,\, \frac{\partial u}{\partial \xi},\, \frac{\partial u}{\partial \eta}\right). \tag{8.15}$$

This is the *canonical form of an equation of the parabolic type.*

3. $B^2 - AC < 0$. Equation (8.1) is of the elliptic type in the domain $D$. We shall suppose that the coefficients $A$, $B$ and $C$ are analytical functions of $x$ and $y$. The coefficients of equations (8.8a) and (8.8b) are also analytical functions of $x$ and $y$ and we may suppose that equation (8.8a) has the analytical solution

$$\varphi(x, y) = \varphi_1(x, y) + i\varphi_2(x, y)$$

in the vicinity of $(x_0, y_0)$, and that $|\partial\varphi/\partial x| + |\partial\varphi/\partial y| \neq 0$ in this region.* Let

$$\xi = \varphi_1(x, y), \quad \eta = \varphi_2(x, y)$$

in the transformation (8.3). It is easy to show that

$$D(\varphi_1, \varphi_2)/D(x, y) \neq 0.$$

If we now separate the real and imaginary parts in the identity

$$A\left(\frac{\partial \varphi}{\partial x}\right)^2 + 2B\,\frac{\partial \varphi}{\partial x}\,\frac{\partial \varphi}{\partial y} + C\left(\frac{\partial \varphi}{\partial y}\right)^2 = 0$$

we obtain

$$A\left(\frac{\partial \xi}{\partial x}\right)^2 + 2B\,\frac{\partial \xi}{\partial x}\,\frac{\partial \xi}{\partial y}\,C + \left(\frac{\partial \eta}{\partial y}\right)^2 =$$

$$= A\left(\frac{\partial \eta}{\partial x}\right)^2 + 2B\,\frac{\partial \eta}{\partial x}\,\frac{\partial \eta}{\partial y} + C\left(\frac{\partial \eta}{\partial y}\right)^2,$$

$$A\,\frac{\partial \xi}{\partial x}\,\frac{\partial \eta}{\partial x} + B\left(\frac{\partial \xi}{\partial x}\,\frac{\partial \eta}{\partial y} + \frac{\partial \xi}{\partial y}\,\frac{\partial \eta}{\partial x}\right) + C\,\frac{\partial \xi}{\partial y}\,\frac{\partial \eta}{\partial y} = 0.$$

---

* The existence of this analytical solution is a consequence of a theorem established by Kovalevskaya [2].

In view of (8.6), it follows that $\bar{A} = \bar{C}, \bar{B} = 0$.
Since the quadratic form

$$At_1^2 + 2Bt_1t_2 + Ct_2^2 \qquad (B^2 - AC < 0)$$

is definite, $\bar{A} = \bar{C}$ can vanish only if

$$\frac{\partial \xi}{\partial x} = \frac{\partial \xi}{\partial y} = \frac{\partial \eta}{\partial x} = \frac{\partial \eta}{\partial y} = 0. \tag{8.16}$$

We have, however, chosen the solution $\varphi(x, y)$, so that the equations in (8.16) are not satisfied at the same time. It follows that $\bar{A} = = \bar{C} \neq 0$ in equation (8.5), and if we divide by $\bar{A}$ we shall reduce it to the form

$$\frac{\partial^2 u}{\partial \xi^2} + \frac{\partial^2 u}{\partial \eta^2} = F_3 \left( \xi, \eta, u, \frac{\partial u}{\partial \xi}, \frac{\partial u}{\partial \eta} \right). \tag{8.17}$$

This is the *canonical form of an equation of the elliptic type*.
*Remark.* It may turn out that equation (8.1) is of a different type in different parts of the domain $D$. As has already been pointed out, equation (8.1) is of the parabolic type at all points at which

$$B^2 - AC = 0. \tag{8.18}$$

We shall suppose that the set of points in $D$ which is described by (8.18) forms a simple smooth curve $\sigma$ which is called the *curve of parabolic degeneracy*. If the curve $\sigma$ divides the domain $D$ into two parts, in one of which equation (7.1) is of the elliptic type and in the other of the hyperbolic type, then we shall say that in the domain $D$ equation (7.1) is of the *mixed type*.
(1) The Tricomi equation

$$y \frac{\partial^2 u}{\partial x^2} + \frac{\partial^2 u}{\partial y^2} = 0$$

is an equation of the mixed type in any domain $D$ containing points on the $x$-axis. For $y > 0$ it is of the elliptic type, for $y < 0$ it is of the hyperbolic type, and for $y = 0$ it is the curve of parabolic degeneracy.
(2) The equation

$$\frac{\partial^2 u}{\partial x^2} + y \frac{\partial^2 u}{\partial y^2} = 0$$

is of the mixed type in any domain $D$ containing points on the $x$-axis; $y = 0$ is the curve of parabolic degeneracy, which is also the characteristic ($y = 0$ is the envelope of the family of characteristics).

**Example:** Consider the equation

$$\frac{\partial^2 u}{\partial x^2} - 2 \sin x \, \frac{\partial^2 u}{\partial x \, \partial y} - \cos^2 x \, \frac{\partial^2 u}{\partial y^2} - \cos x \, \frac{\partial u}{\partial y} = 0; \qquad (8.19)$$

which is of the hyperbolic type, since

$$B^2 - AC = \sin^2 x + \cos^2 x = 1 > 0.$$

Equation (8.9a) now becomes

$$dy^2 + 2 \sin x \, dx \, dy - \cos^2 x \, dx^2 = 0$$

or

$$dy + (1 + \sin x) \, dx = 0, \quad dy - (1 - \sin x) \, dx = 0.$$

On integrating these equations, we obtain

$$x + y - \cos x = C_1, \quad x - y + \cos x = C_2.$$

Substituting

$$\xi = x + y - \cos x, \quad \eta = x - y + \cos x$$

into (8.19) we obtain

$$\frac{\partial^2 u}{\partial \xi \, \partial \eta} = 0. \qquad (8.20)$$

The substitution $\xi = \alpha + \beta$, $\eta = \alpha - \beta$ will reduce equation (8.20) to the canonical form

$$\frac{\partial^2 u}{\partial \alpha^2} - \frac{\partial^2 u}{\partial \beta^2} = 0.$$

Equation (8.19) may be integrated in a closed form, i.e. it is possible to find a formula giving all the solutions to these equations. In point of fact, let us rewrite equation (8.20) in the form

$$\frac{\partial}{\partial \xi} \left( \frac{\partial u}{\partial \eta} \right) = 0.$$

in which case

$$\frac{\partial u}{\partial \eta} = \theta(\eta),$$

where $\theta(\eta)$ is an arbitrary function of $\eta$. Integrating the resulting equation with respect to $\eta$ with $\xi$ as a parameter, we find that

$$u = \int \theta(\eta) \, d\eta + \varphi(\xi),$$

where $\varphi(\xi)$ is an arbitrary function of $\xi$. If we let

$$\int \theta(\eta) \, d\eta = \psi(\eta),$$

we obtain

$$u = \varphi(\xi) + \psi(\eta)$$

or, returning to the old variables $(x, y)$, we obtain the solution of equation (8.19) in the form

$$u(x, y) = \varphi(x + y - \cos x) + \psi(x - y + \cos x).$$

**Problems.** Reduce the following equations to the canonical form

1) $\dfrac{\partial^2 u}{\partial x^2} - 2 \cos x \, \dfrac{\partial^2 u}{\partial x \, \partial y} - (3 + \sin^2 x) \dfrac{\partial^2 u}{\partial y^2} - y \dfrac{\partial u}{\partial y} = 0;$

2) $\dfrac{\partial^2 u}{\partial x^2} - 2x \, \dfrac{\partial^2 u}{\partial x \, \partial y} + x^2 \dfrac{\partial^2 u}{\partial y^2} - 2 \dfrac{\partial u}{\partial y} = 0;$

3) $(1 + x^2) \dfrac{\partial^2 u}{\partial x^2} + (1 + y^2) \dfrac{\partial^2 u}{\partial y^2} + x \dfrac{\partial u}{\partial x} + y \dfrac{\partial u}{\partial y} = 0.$

**Answers.**

1) $\dfrac{\partial^2 u}{\partial \xi \, \partial \eta} + \dfrac{\eta - \xi}{32} \left( \dfrac{\partial u}{\partial \xi} - \dfrac{\partial u}{\partial \eta} \right) = 0, \quad \xi = 2x + \sin x + y,$

$\eta = 2x - \sin x - y;$

2) $\dfrac{\partial^2 u}{\partial \eta^2} - \dfrac{\partial u}{\partial \xi} = 0, \quad \xi = \dfrac{x^2}{2} + y, \quad \eta = x;$

3) $\dfrac{\partial^2 u}{\partial \xi^2} + \dfrac{\partial^2 u}{\partial \eta^2} = 0, \quad \xi = \ln (x + \sqrt{1 + x^2}),$

$\eta = \ln (y + \sqrt{1 + y^2}).$

Chapter 3

# EQUATIONS OF THE HYPERBOLIC TYPE

Problems involving oscillatory processes, for example the oscillations of strings, membranes, gases, electromagnetic fields, and so
on, lead to equations of the hyperbolic type. A characteristic feature
of processes described by such equations is a finite velocity of
propagation.

### § 9. Oscillations of a string: d'Alambert's solution

**1. Infinite string.** The equation for the free oscillations of a uniform
string is

$$\frac{\partial^2 u}{\partial t^2} = a^2 \frac{\partial^2 u}{\partial x^2}, \quad a = \sqrt{\frac{T}{\rho}}. \tag{9.1}$$

Let us substitute

$$\xi = x - at, \quad \eta = x + at. \tag{9.2}$$

It is readily seen that $x - at = c_1$, $x + at = c_2$ are the characteristics of equation (9.1). In terms of the new variables, equation
(9.1) becomes

$$\frac{\partial^2 u}{\partial \xi \partial \eta} = 0$$

or, if we rewrite it in the form

$$\frac{\partial}{\partial \eta}\left(\frac{\partial u}{\partial \xi}\right) = 0,$$

we have

$$\frac{\partial u}{\partial \xi} = \omega(\xi),$$

where $\omega(\xi)$ is an arbitrary function of $\xi$. Integrating the resulting equation with respect to $\xi$ and regarding $\eta$ as a parameter, we find that

$$u = \int \omega(\xi)\,d\xi + \theta_2(\eta),$$

where $\theta_2(\eta)$ is an arbitrary function of $\eta$. If we now let

$$\int \omega(\xi)\,d\xi = \theta_1(\xi),$$

we obtain

$$u = \theta_1(\xi) + \theta_2(\eta).$$

and if we return to the old variables $(x, t)$ we have

$$u(x, t) = \theta_1(x - at) + \theta_2(x + at). \tag{9.3}$$

It can readily be verified that the function $u(x, t)$ given by (9.3) is a solution of equation (9.1) if $\theta_1$ and $\theta_2$ are arbitrary twice-differentiable functions. The solution (9.3) of equation (9.1) is known as *d'Alambert's solution*. To elucidate the physical meaning of (9.3), let us consider to begin with the special case of the oscillations of a string when $\theta_2 \equiv 0$, i.e. when the displacement of the string is given by

$$u_1 = \theta_1(x - at). \tag{9.4}$$

We shall suppose that an observer leaves the point $x = c$ on the string at time $t = 0$ and moves in the positive direction of the $x$-axis with the velocity $a$, i.e. its $x$-coordinate is given by $x = c + at$ or $x - at = c$. For this particular observer, the displacement of the string given by (9.4) will remain constant and given by $\theta_1(c)$. The function $u_1 = \theta_1(x - at)$ is said to describe the propagation of the forward wave. It follows that the solution given by (9.4) represents the forward wave which propagates in the positive direction of the $x$-axis with velocity $a$. In the same way, the function $u_2 = \theta_2(x + at)$ represents the wave travelling in the opposite direction, i.e. in the direction of the negative $x$-axis, with a velocity $a$. The solution given by (9.3) is therefore the sum of these two waves.

This leads to the following graphical method of finding the form of the string at any time $t$. We first plot the curves

$$u_1 = \theta_1(x), \quad u_2 = \theta_2(x),$$

which represent the forward and reverse waves at the initial time $t = 0$, and then without changing their form we displace them simultaneously with velocity $a$ in opposite directions, i.e. $u_1 = \theta_1(x)$ to the right and $u_2 = \theta_2(x)$ to the left. In order to obtain the shape of the string, all that is necessary is to add the ordinates of the two curves algebraically.

Let us now consider the upper half-plane $x, t$ in which the $x$-axis represents the position of the string at the initial time $t = 0$. Any point $(x, t)$ on this half-plane represents a definite point $x$ of the string at a particular time $t$. It is quite easy to find graphically those points on the string whose initial displacements have reached a point $x_0$ at time $t_0$. In view of the above analysis, these points will have the abscissae $x + at_0$, since $a$ is the velocity of propagation of the disturbance. To find them on the $x$-axis it is sufficient to draw through the point $(x_0, t_0)$ the two characteristics

$$x - at = x_0 - at_0, \quad x + at = x_0 + at_0, \tag{9.5}$$

and from their intersection with the $x$-axis obtain the required points (fig. 3).

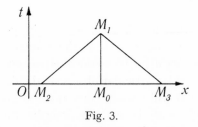

Fig. 3.

The function $\theta_1(x - at)$ retains a constant value along the first characteristic, i.e. this line yields the values of $(x, t)$ for which the forward wave gives the same displacement as at $(x_0, t_0)$. The second characteristic in (9.5) plays the same role for the reverse wave $\theta_2(x + at)$. We thus see that the disturbance propagates along the characteristics.

**2. Cauchy's problem.** It is required to find the solution of (9.1) subject to the initial conditions

$$u|_{t=0} = \varphi_0(x), \quad \frac{\partial u}{\partial t}\bigg|_{t=0} = \varphi_1(x). \tag{9.6}$$

Since the string is infinite, the functions $\varphi_0(x)$ and $\varphi_1(x)$ are given at $(-\infty, \infty)$.

In the solution (9.3) of equation (9.1) we must choose the functions $\theta_1$ and $\theta_2$ so that they will satisfy the initial conditions (9.6). From (9.6) we have

$$\varphi_0(x) = \theta_1(x) + \theta_2(x), \quad \varphi_1(x) = -a[\theta_1'(x) - \theta_2'(x)],$$

and hence, on integrating the second equation, we obtain

$$\theta_1(x) + \theta_2(x) = \varphi_0(x),$$

$$\theta_1(x) - \theta_2(x) = -\frac{1}{a}\int\limits_0^x \varphi_1(z)\,dz + C, \tag{9.7}$$

where $C$ is an arbitrary constant.

From equations (9.7) we have

$$\theta_1(x) = \tfrac{1}{2}\varphi_0(x) - \frac{1}{2a}\int\limits_0^x \varphi_1(z)\,dz + \frac{C}{2},$$

$$\theta_2(x) = \tfrac{1}{2}\varphi_0(x) + \frac{1}{2a}\int\limits_0^x \varphi_1(z)\,dz - \frac{C}{2}, \tag{9.8}$$

and on substituting this into (9.3) we have

$$u(x,\,t) = \tfrac{1}{2}\varphi_0(x - at) - \frac{1}{2a}\int\limits_0^{x-at} \varphi_1(z)\,dz + \frac{C}{2} +$$

$$+\; \tfrac{1}{2}\varphi_0(x + at) + \frac{1}{2a}\int\limits_0^{x+at} \varphi_1(z)\,dz - \frac{C}{2}$$

or, finally,

$$u(x, t) = \frac{\varphi_0(x - at) + \varphi_0(x + at)}{2} + \frac{1}{2a} \int\limits_{x-at}^{x+at} \varphi_1(z)\, dz. \qquad (9.9)$$

The latter is the solution of Cauchy's problem (9.1), (9.6) if $\varphi_0(x)$ has continuous first-order and second-order derivatives and $\varphi_1(x)$ has continuous first-order derivatives. It is evident that the above formulation of Cauchy's problem is correct. The fact that the solution is unique follows from the way in which (9.9) was derived. There is also no doubt that the solution given by (9.9) depends continuously on the initial conditions. In point of fact, for any $\varepsilon > 0$ it is possible to find $\delta > 0$ such that if we replace $\varphi_0(x)$ and $\varphi_1(x)$ by $\bar{\varphi}_0(x)$ and $\bar{\varphi}_1(x)$ in such a way that

$$|\varphi_0(x) - \bar{\varphi}_0(x)| < \delta, \quad |\varphi_1(x) - \bar{\varphi}_1(x)| < \delta \quad (-\infty < x < \infty),$$

then the absolute magnitude of the difference between the new solution $\bar{u}(x, t)$ and the initial solution $u(x, t)$ will be less than $\varepsilon$ in any finite interval of time. This result can readily be established from (9.9).

Consider the following two special cases.

(1) Initial velocities of all points on the string are zero, and the initial displacement is introduced only within the finite interval $(-\alpha, \alpha)$, i.e. $\varphi_0(x) = 0$ outside this interval. The solution given by (9.9) then becomes

$$u(x, t) = \frac{\varphi_0(x - at) + \varphi_0(x + at)}{2}. \qquad (9.10)$$

As can be seen, this is the sum of two waves, one travelling to the right and the other to the left, with velocity $a$. The initial form of each wave is described by the function $\frac{1}{2}\varphi_0(x)$, i.e. one-half of the initial displacement. If the point $x$ on the string lies to the right of the interval $(-\alpha, \alpha)$, i.e. $x > \alpha$, then for $t < (x - \alpha)/a$ it follows from the form of the function $\varphi_0(x)$ and from equation (9.10) that $u(x, t) = 0$, i.e. the wave has not reached the point $x$. This point will first undergo oscillations, i.e. the wave front of the direct wave will reach it at time $t = (x - \alpha)/a$. When $t > (x + \alpha)/a$ it follows from (9.10) that $u(x, t) \equiv 0$. The time $t = (x + \alpha)/a$ corresponds to the passage of the trailing edge of the direct wave through the point $x$. Thereafter $u(x, t)$ remains equal to zero. A similar analysis can be given for points lying inside the interval $(-\alpha, \alpha)$ or to the left of this interval. It follows that after the two waves have passed through a given point (or in the case of points outside the range of the initial displacement, after the passage of only one wave) there is no displacement at all and the string remains at rest.

(2) Initial displacement equal to zero and $\varphi_1(x) \neq 0$ only in a finite interval $(-\alpha, \alpha)$. In this case, the solution given by (9.9) assumes the form

$$u(x, t) = \frac{1}{2a} \int\limits_{x-at}^{x+at} \varphi_1(z)\, dz \qquad (9.11)$$

or, substituting

$$\frac{1}{2a} \int\limits_{0}^{x} \varphi_1(z)\, dz = \psi(x),$$

we obtain

$$u(x, t) = \psi(x + at) - \psi(x - at),$$

i.e. we have two waves, one travelling to the right and one to the left. Let us consider the solution given by (9.11) in greater detail. Suppose that the point $x$ on the string lies to the right of the interval $(-\alpha, \alpha)$. When $t = 0$ the range of integration $(x - at, x + at)$ degenerates to the point $x$ and then as $t$ increases it extends to either side with velocity $a$. When $t < (x - \alpha)/a$ it has no common points with $(-\alpha, \alpha)$, the function $\varphi_1(z)$ vanishes inside it, and equation (9.11) yields $u(x, t) = 0$, i.e. the point $x$ remains at rest. From time $t = (x - \alpha)/a$ onwards, the interval $(x - at, x + at)$ will overlap with $(-\alpha, \alpha)$, in which $\varphi_1(z)$ is non-zero, and the point $x$ will undergo oscillations (passage of the leading front of the wave through the point $x$). Finally, when $t > (x + \alpha)/a$ the interval $(x - at, x + at)$ will contain the entire interval $(-\alpha, \alpha)$ and the integration over $(x - at, x + at)$ will reduce to integration over $(-\alpha, \alpha)$, since outside this interval $\varphi_1(z) = 0$, i.e. for $t > (x + \alpha)/a$

the function $u(x, t)$ assumes the constant value

$$\frac{1}{2a} \int_{-\alpha}^{\alpha} \varphi_1(z)\, dz. \tag{9.12}$$

The trailing edge of the wave passes through the point $x$ at time $t = (x + \alpha)/a$.

We thus see that the initial impulse ensures that points on the string are displaced by the amount given by (9.12) and remain in this new position, i.e. the waves leave a "trail" behind them.

**3. Finite string.** Now consider a string of given length $l$ which is fixed at the ends. We must find the solution of the wave equation

$$\frac{\partial^2 u}{\partial t^2} = a^2 \frac{\partial^2 u}{\partial x^2} \tag{9.13}$$

subject to the boundary conditions

$$u|_{x=0} = 0, \quad u|_{x=l} = 0 \tag{9.14}$$

and the initial conditions

$$u|_{t=0} = \varphi_0(x), \quad \frac{\partial u}{\partial t}\bigg|_{t=0} = \varphi_1(x) \qquad (0 \leqslant x \leqslant l). \tag{9.15}$$

D'Alambert's solution

$$u(x, t) = \theta_1(x - at) + \theta_2(x + at), \tag{9.16}$$

remains satisfactory, but the definition of $\theta_1$ and $\theta_2$ through the formulae

$$\theta_1(x) = \tfrac{1}{2}\varphi_0(x) - \frac{1}{2a} \int_0^x \varphi_1(z)\, dz,$$

$$\theta_2(x) = \tfrac{1}{2}\varphi_0(x) + \frac{1}{2a} \int_0^x \varphi_1(z)\, dz \tag{9.17}$$

encounters the difficulty that the functions $\varphi_0(x)$ and $\varphi_1(x)$, and therefore $\theta_1(x)$ and $\theta_2(x)$, are defined only in the interval $(0, l)$, which is in accordance with the physical interpretation of the problem, whilst the arguments $x \pm at$ in (9.16) may lie outside this interval. It thus seems necessary to continue the functions $\theta_1(x)$ and $\theta_2(x)$, or, which is the same thing, continue the functions $\varphi_0(x)$ and $\varphi_1(x)$ outside the interval $(0, l)$. From the physical point of view this continuation may be reduced to the determination of the initial displacement of an *infinite* string, which ensures that the motion of the segment $(0, l)$ is the same as for a string with fixed ends, the remainder of the string being ignored.

To continue the functions $\varphi_0(x)$ and $\varphi_1(x)$ we shall use the boundary conditions (9.14). Substituting $x = 0$ and $x = l$ into the right-hand side of (9.16), and recalling the boundary conditions given by (9.14), we obtain

$$\theta_1(-at) + \theta_2(at) = 0, \quad \theta_1(l - at) + \theta_2(l + at) = 0$$

or, if we replace $at$ by $x$

$$\theta_1(-x) = -\theta_2(x), \quad \theta_2(l + x) = -\theta_1(l - x). \tag{9.18}$$

When $x$ lies in the interval $(0, l)$, the first of these two formulae defines $\theta_1(x)$ in $(-l, 0)$, whilst the second defines $\theta_2(x)$ in $(l, 2l)$. The two functions $\theta_1(x)$ and $\theta_2(x)$ are thus fully defined in an interval of length $2l$. Moreover, it follows from (9.18) that

$$\theta_2(2l + x) = -\theta_1(-x) = \theta_2(x), \quad \theta_1(2l + x) = \theta_1(x),$$

i.e. the functions $\theta_1(x)$ and $\theta_2(x)$ are periodic with a period of $2l$. The functions $\theta_1(x)$ and $\theta_2(x)$ are thus defined for all real $x$. Since

$$\varphi_0(x) = \theta_1(x) + \theta_2(x), \quad \varphi_1(x) = a[\theta_2'(x) - \theta_1'(x)],$$

we find that

$$\varphi_0(-x) = \theta_1(-x) + \theta_2(-x) = -\theta_2(x) - \theta_1(x) = -\varphi_0(x),$$
$$\varphi_1(-x) = a[\theta_2'(-x) - \theta_2'(-x)] = a[\theta_1'(x) - \theta_2'(x)] = -\varphi_1(x),$$
$$\varphi_0(x + 2l) = \varphi_0(x), \quad \varphi_1(x + 2l) = \varphi_1(x).$$

These formulae show that the functions $\varphi_0(x)$ and $\varphi_1(x)$ may be continued from the interval $(0, l)$ to the interval $(-l, 0)$, where they are odd functions, and thereafter with a period of $2l$.

In order to ensure that the above solution has first-order and second-order derivatives, it is necessary that in addition to being

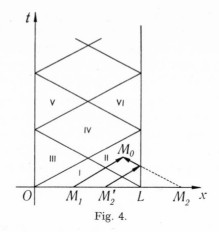

Fig. 4.

differentiable, the functions $\varphi_0(x)$ and $\varphi_1(x)$ must obey the following conditions

$$\varphi_0(0) = \varphi_0(l) = 0, \quad \varphi_0''(0) = \varphi_0''(l) = 0, \quad \varphi_1(0) = \varphi_1(l) = 0.$$

These represent the compatibility of the initial and boundary conditions.

Let us now consider the effect which the fixing of two ends of the string has on its oscillations. To do this, let us return to the $(x, t)$ half-plane. Since the string has a finite length, we must consider only a band in the upper half-plane $t > 0$ lying between $x = 0$ and $x = l$ (fig. 4). If we draw the characteristics through the points 0 and $l$ until they meet the boundaries of the band, and then continue them as shown in fig. 4, we will divide the band into regions I, II, III, ..., and so on.

Points in region I correspond to times $t$ at which points on the string are reached by the forward and reverse waves which have originated at the internal points on the string. It follows that in this region the addition of the fictitious infinite lengths of string on either side of the interval $(0, l)$ has no effect on the oscillations.

Points outside region I correspond to those times $t$ at which points on the actual string are traversed by waves originating on the fictitious sections. Consider, for example, the point $M_0(x_0, t_0)$ in region II. Since

$$u(x_0, t_0) = \theta_1(x_0 - at_0) + \theta_2(x_0 + at_0),$$

there are two waves at this point: a direct wave originating at the initially undisturbed point $M_1$ with $x = x_0 - at_0$, and a reverse wave from the point $M_2$ with $x = x_0 + at_0$. In this case $M_1$ is a real point on the string and $M_2$ a fictitious point. It is quite easy to replace the latter by a real point by noting that in view of (9.18)

$$\theta_2(x_0 + at_0) = \theta_2(l + x_0 + at_0 - l) = -\theta_1(2l - x_0 - at_0)$$

and thus the reverse wave $\theta_2(x_0 + at_0)$ is simply the direct wave $-\theta_1(2l - x_0 - at_0)$ originating from the initially disturbed point $M_2'(2l - x_0 - at_0)$, which is symmetric to $M_2$ with respect to the point $L$. When this wave reaches the end of the string at time

$$t = \frac{l - (2l - x_0 - at_0)}{a} = \frac{x_0 + at_0 - l}{a},$$

it changes its direction and sign and arrives at $M_0$ at time $t_0$.
Therefore, the fact that the string is fixed at $x = l$ gives rise to the reflection of the wave, which is associated with a change in sign of the displacement at constant absolute magnitude.
A similar phenomenon occurs at the other end of the string $(x = 0)$. At points in region III we have two waves: a direct wave and a reverse wave reflected at $x = 0$. In regions IV, V, VI, and so on there are waves which have undergone several such reflections at both ends of the string. It follows from the above analysis that the oscillations of a string fixed at both ends is periodic with a period of $2l/a$.

**Problems** (1) An infinite string $x > 0$ is in a state of equilibrium. At time $t > 0$ the point $x = 0$ undergoes a small simple harmonic oscillation $A \sin \omega t$. Show that the displacement at points $x > 0$ is given by

$$u(x, t) = \begin{cases} 0 & t < \dfrac{x}{a}, \\ A \sin \omega \left( t - \dfrac{x}{a} \right) & t > \dfrac{x}{a}. \end{cases}$$

(2) A uniform string fixed at $x = 0$ and $x = l$ takes the form of a parabola at time $t = 0$. The parabola is symmetric about the perpendicular drawn through the point $x = l/2$. Determine the form of the string at times $t = l/2a$ and $t = l/a$, assuming that the initial velocities are zero.

## § 10. Hyperbolic equation with two independent variables

Consider the equation

$$L(u) \equiv \frac{\partial^2 u}{\partial x \partial y} + a(x, y) \frac{\partial u}{\partial x} + b(x, y) \frac{\partial u}{\partial y} +$$

$$+ c(x, y)u = f(x, y). \tag{10.1}$$

We saw in Chapter II § 8 that a linear hyperbolic equation with two independent variables could be reduced to this form [$a(x, y)$, $b(x, y)$, $c(x, y)$ and $f(x, y)$ are continuous functions]. The equation of characteristics for (10.1) is

$$\frac{\partial \omega}{\partial x} \frac{\partial \omega}{\partial y} = 0 \quad \text{or} \quad \frac{\partial \omega}{\partial x} = 0, \quad \frac{\partial \omega}{\partial y} = 0.$$

These equations have the solutions $y$ and $x$ respectively, and therefore $x = \text{const}$ and $y = \text{const}$ are the characteristics of equation (10.1).

**1. Cauchy's problem.** Suppose that we are given an arc of a curve $l$ in the $x, y$-plane which intersects any straight line parallel to the coordinate axes at not more than one point. The equation of this arc may be written in the form $y = g(x)$ or $x = h(y)$. We shall suppose that the derivatives $g'(x)$ and $h'(y)$ exist and are not zero. Suppose that the values of $u$ and $\partial u/\partial y$ along the curve $l$ are given by

$$u|_{y=g(x)} = \varphi_0(x), \quad \frac{\partial u}{\partial y}\bigg|_{y=g(x)} = \varphi_1(x). \tag{10.2}$$

These conditions enables us to find the values of $\partial u/\partial x$ on the curve $y = g(x)$. In fact, if we differentiate the first condition in

(10.2) with respect to $x$, we obtain

$$\frac{\partial u}{\partial x}\Big|_{y=g(x)} + \frac{\partial u}{\partial y}\Big|_{y=g(x)} g'(x) = \varphi_0'(x),$$

and hence

$$\frac{\partial u}{\partial x}\Big|_{y=g(x)} = \varphi_0'(x) - \varphi_1(x)\, g'(x) = \omega(x). \tag{10.3}$$

Cauchy's problem is formulated as follows: *it is required to find the solution of* (10.1) *in the vicinity of the curve l which satisfies the conditions given by* (10.2).

If we substitute

$$v = \frac{\partial u}{\partial x}, \qquad w = \frac{\partial u}{\partial y} \tag{10.4}$$

into (10.1), the latter becomes equivalent to the set of three equations

$$\frac{\partial v}{\partial y} = f(x, y) - av - bw - cu,$$

$$\frac{\partial w}{\partial x} = f(x, y) - av - bw - cu, \tag{10.5}$$

$$\frac{\partial u}{\partial y} = w.$$

Let us take an arbitrary point $N(x, y)$ in the rectangle $ABCD$ in fig. 5 and draw the characteristics $NP$ and $NQ$ through it until

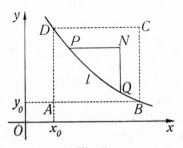

Fig. 5.

they intersect the curve $l$. Integrating the first and third equations in (10.5) along the straight line $QN$ and the second along $PN$, and using (10.2), (10.3) and (10.4), we obtain

$$v(x, y) = \omega(x) + \int_{g(x)}^{y} [f(x, y) - av - bw - cu]\, dy,$$

$$w(x, y) = \varphi_1(x) + \int_{h(y)}^{x} [f(x, y) - av - bw - cu]\, dx, \qquad (10.6)$$

$$u(x, y) = \varphi_0(x) + \int_{g(x)}^{y} w(x, y)\, dy.$$

It is evident that if $u(x, y)$ is a solution of (10.1) which satisfies the conditions given by (10.2), then the functions $v$, $w$ and $u$ will satisfy the set of integral equations given by (10.6). Conversely, a continuous solution $(u, v, w)$ of the set of equations given by (10.6) will clearly satisfy the set of differential equations in (10.5), and the function $u(x, y)$ will satisfy (10.1) and the conditions given by (10.2). In fact, from the third equation in (10.6) we have $\partial u/\partial y = w$. Moreover, using (10.4), (10.5), (10.3), and the first equation in (10.6) we have

$$\frac{\partial u}{\partial x} = \varphi_0'(x) - w(x, y)|_{y=g(x)}\, g'(x) + \int_{g(x)}^{y} \frac{\partial w}{\partial x}\, dy =$$

$$= \varphi_0'(x) - \frac{\partial u}{\partial y}\bigg|_{y=g(x)} g'(x) + \int_{g(x)}^{y} [f(x, y) - av - bw - cu]\, dy =$$

$$= \varphi_0'(x) - \varphi_1(x) g'(x) + \int_{g(x)}^{y} [f(x, y) - av - bw - cu]\, dy =$$

$$= \omega(x) + \int_{g(x)}^{y} [f(x, y) - av - bw - cu]\, dy = v.$$

We thus see that both equations in (10.4) are satisfied. By substituting (10.4) into the first equation in (10.5), we can verify that the function $u(x, y)$ satisfies (10.1). It is easy to see that $u(x, y)$ will also satisfy the conditions given by (10.2).

Cauchy's problem (10.1)–(10.2) has thus been reduced to the proof

of the existence of a continuous solution of the set of integral
equations given by (10.6).

The solution of (10.6) will be sought by the method of successive
approximations. Let us take

$$v_0 = \omega(x), \quad w_0 = \varphi_1(x), \quad u_0 = \varphi_0(x),$$

as the zero-order approximation. Higher-order approximations will
be calculated from

$$v_n(x, y) = \omega(x) +$$

$$+ \int_{g(x)}^{y} [f(x, y) - av_{n-1} - bw_{n-1} - cu_{n-1}] \, dy,$$

$$w_n(x, y) = \varphi_1(x) +$$

$$+ \int_{h(y)}^{x} [f(x, y) - av_{n-1} - bw_{n-1} - cu_{n-1}] \, dx, \qquad (10.7)$$

$$u_n(x, y) = \varphi_0(x) + \int_{g(x)}^{y} w_{n-1}(x, y) \, dy$$

$$(n = 1, 2, 3, \ldots).$$

We shall now prove that the sequence $\{v_n, w_n, u_n\}$ converges
uniformly in the curvilinear triangle $BCD$ in fig. 5.
We have

$$v_{n+1} - v_n =$$

$$= - \int_{g(x)}^{y} [a(v_n - v_{n-1}) + b(w_n - w_{n-1}) + c(u_n - u_{n-1})] \, dy,$$

$$w_{n+1} - w_n = \qquad (10.8)$$

$$= - \int_{h(y)}^{x} [a(v_n - v_{n-1}) + b(w_n - w_{n-1}) + c(u_n - u_{n-1})] \, dx,$$

$$u_{n+1} - u_n = \int_{g(x)}^{y} (w_n - w_{n-1}) \, dy.$$

We shall show that the differences $|v_n - v_{n-1}|$, $|w_n - w_{n-1}|$,

$|u_n - u_{n-1}|$ satisfy the inequalities

$$|v_n - v_{n-1}| \leqslant K^{n-1}A \; \frac{(x + y - x_0 - y_0)^{n-1}}{(n-1)!} \; ,$$

$$|w_n - w_{n-1}| \leqslant K^{n-1}A \; \frac{(x + y - x_0 - y_0)^{n-1}}{(n-1)!} \; , \qquad (10.9)$$

$$|u_n - u_{n-1}| \leqslant K^{n-1}A \; \frac{(x + y - x_0 - y_0)^{n-1}}{(n-1)!} \; ,$$

where $M = (\max/BCD)[|a| + |b| + |c|]$, $K = \max(1, M)$, and $A$ is a constant. The validity of (10.9) is obvious when $n = 1$ if $A$ is chosen to be large enough. We shall show that these inequalities remain valid when $n$ is replaced by $n + 1$. For example, from (10.8) we have

$$|v_{n+1} - v_n| \leqslant \int_{g(x)}^{y} (|a| + |b| + |c|)K^{n-1}A \; \frac{(x+y-x_0-y_0)^{n-1}}{(n-1)!} \; dy \leqslant$$

$$\leqslant K^n A \int_{y_0}^{y} \frac{(x + y - x_0 - y_0)^{n-1}}{(n-1)!} \; dy =$$

$$= K^n A \left[ \frac{(x + y - x_0 - y_0)^n}{n!} - \frac{(x - x_0)^n}{n!} \right] \leqslant$$

$$\leqslant K^n A \; \frac{(x + y - x_0 - y_0)^n}{n!} \qquad (x > x_0, \, y_0 \leqslant g(x) \leqslant b).$$

The other differences can be estimated in precisely the same way. It is evident from (10.9) that the series

$$v_0 + \sum_{n=1}^{\infty} (v_n - v_{n-1}), \quad w_0 + \sum_{n=1}^{\infty} (w_n - w_{n-1}),$$

$$u_0 + \sum_{n=1}^{\infty} (u_n - u_{n-1}),$$

whose terms are smaller in absolute magnitude than the terms of the uniformly convergent series

$$A + A \sum_{n=2}^{\infty} K^{n-1} \frac{(x + y - x_0 - y_0)^{n-1}}{(n-1)!} = A(1 + e^{K(x+y-x_0-y_0)}).$$

are absolutely and uniformly convergent. It follows that the next approximation $v_n$, $w_n$, and $u_n$ in the curvilinear triangle $BCD$ tends uniformly to definite limits $v$, $w$, and $u$ respectively. The limiting functions are continuous, since all the successive approximations are continuous. On passing to the limit in (10.7) we find that limiting functions $v(x, y)$, $w(x, y)$, and $u(x, y)$ satisfy the set of equations given by (10.6).

*Uniqueness of the solution of* (10.6).

Let us suppose that we have two different continuous solutions of (10.6), and let us denote them by $v_1, w_1, u_1$ and $v_2, w_2, u_2$. The differences $V = v_1 - v_2$, $W = w_1 - w_2$, and $U = u_1 - u_2$ satisfy the homogeneous set of equations

$$V(x, y) = - \int_{g(x)}^{y} (aV + bW + cU) \, dy,$$

$$W(x, y) = - \int_{h(y)}^{x} (aV + bW + cU) \, dx, \qquad (10.10)$$

$$U(x, y) = \int_{g(x)}^{y} W(x, y) \, dy.$$

We must show that $V = W = U = 0$. The functions $V$, $W$, and $U$ are continuous and bounded, since they are differences between functions which are continuous inside the curvilinear triangle $BCD$. This means that there exists a constant $B$ such that

$$|V| \leqslant B, \quad |W| \leqslant B, \quad |U| \leqslant B.$$

From (10.10) we have

$$|V(x, y)| \leqslant \int_{g(x)}^{y} (|a| + |b| + |c|) B \, dy \leqslant$$

$$\leqslant KB(y - y_0) \leqslant KB \frac{(x + y - x_0 - y_0)}{1!},$$

$$|W(x,y)| \leqslant KB \frac{(x+y-x_0-y_0)}{1!},$$

$$|U(x,y)| \leqslant KB \frac{(x+y-x_0-y_0)}{1!}.$$

Using the method of mathematical induction, we obtain

$$|V| \leqslant K^n B \frac{(x+y-x_0-y_0)^n}{n!}, \quad |W| \leqslant K^n B \frac{(x+y-x_0-y_0)^n}{n!},$$

$$|U| \leqslant K^n B \frac{(x+y-x_0-y_0)^n}{n!}$$

which are valid for any $n$. Hence, it follows that $V = W = U = 0$, i.e. $v_1 = v_2$, $w_1 = w_2$, and $u_1 = u_2$.

**2. Goursat's problem.** It is required to find the solution of (10.1) which assumes the following values on the characteristics $x = x_0$ and $y = y_0$:

$$u|_{x=x_0} = \varphi_1(y), \quad y_0 \leqslant y \leqslant b,$$
$$u|_{y=y_0} = \varphi_2(x), \quad x_0 \leqslant x \leqslant a. \tag{10.11}$$

We shall suppose that $\varphi_1(y)$ and $\varphi_2(x)$ have continuous first-order derivatives and $\varphi_1(y_0) = \varphi_2(x_0)$.
As in Cauchy's problem, let

$$v = \frac{\partial u}{\partial x}, \quad w = \frac{\partial u}{\partial y}. \tag{10.12}$$

Equation (10.1) will then become equivalent to the following set of three equations

$$\frac{\partial v}{\partial y} = f(x,y) - a(x,y)v - b(x,y)w - c(x,y)u,$$

$$\frac{\partial w}{\partial x} = f(x,y) - a(x,y)v - b(x,y)w - c(x,y)u, \tag{10.13}$$

$$\frac{\partial u}{\partial y} = w.$$

If we recall (10.2) and (10.3), it follows from these that

$$v(x, y) = \varphi_2'(x) + \int_{y_0}^{y} [f(x, y) - av - bw - cu]\, dy,$$

$$w(x, y) = \varphi_1'(y) + \int_{x_0}^{x} [f(x, y) - av - bw - cu]\, dx, \qquad (10.14)$$

$$u(x, y) = \varphi_2(x) + \int_{y_0}^{y} w\, dy.$$

As in Cauchy's problem, we have shown that Goursat's problem (10.1)–(10.11) reduces to proving that there exists a continuous solution of the set of integral equations given by (10.14). As before, the existence and uniqueness of the set given by (10.14) can be established by the method of successive approximations.

## § 11. The wave equation

**1. Poisson's formula.** We shall consider the wave equation

$$\frac{\partial^2 u}{\partial t^2} = a^2 \left( \frac{\partial^2 u}{\partial x^2} + \frac{\partial^2 u}{\partial y^2} + \frac{\partial^2 u}{\partial z^2} \right) \qquad (11.1)$$

and seek its solution subject to the initial conditions

$$u|_{t=0} = \varphi_0(x, y, z), \quad \frac{\partial u}{\partial t}\bigg|_{t=0} = \varphi_1(x, y, z). \qquad (11.2)$$

We shall assume that $\varphi_0(x, y, z)$ and its first, second, and third derivatives are continuous, and that $\varphi_1(x, y, z)$ and its first and second derivatives are continuous in all space. To begin with, we shall show that the integral

$$u(x, y, z, t) = \frac{1}{4\pi a} \iint\limits_{S_{at}} \frac{\varphi(\xi, \eta, \zeta)}{r}\, d\sigma_r, \qquad (11.3)$$

evaluated over the surface $S_{at}$ of a sphere of radius $r = at$ with centre at the point $M(x, y, z)$ is a solution of the wave equation (11.1) where $\varphi(\xi, \eta, \zeta)$ is an arbitrary function.

We note that the coordinates of the points on $S_{at}$ can be written in the form

$$\xi = x + \alpha at, \quad \eta = y + \beta at, \quad \zeta = z + \gamma at,$$

where $(\alpha, \beta, \gamma)$ are the direction cosines of a radius of the sphere $S_{at}$ and can be written in the form

$$\alpha = \sin \theta \cos \psi, \quad \beta = \sin \theta \sin \psi, \quad \gamma = \cos \theta,$$

where $\theta$ varies between 0 and $\pi$, and $\psi$ between 0 and $2\pi$. When the point $(\xi, \eta, \zeta)$ describes the surface $S_{at}$, the point $(\alpha, \beta, \gamma)$ describes the surface $S_1$ of unit radius and centre at the origin of coordinates, and the relation between the elements of area $d\sigma_r$ and $d\sigma_1$ on the two spheres is

$$d\sigma_r = r^2 d\sigma_1 = a^2 t^2 d\sigma_1 = a^2 t^2 \sin \theta \, d\theta \, d\psi.$$

The integral given by (11.3) can thus be reduced to

$$u(x, y, z, t) = \frac{t}{4\pi} \int\!\!\int_{S_1} \varphi(x - \alpha at, y + \beta at, z + \gamma at) \, d\sigma_1. \quad (11.4)$$

Hence, it is easy to see that $u(x, y, z, t)$ has continuous derivatives of order up to $K$ if $\varphi(\xi, \eta, \zeta)$ and its derivatives of order up to $K$ ($K \geqslant 2$) are continuous.

From (11.4) we find that

$$\frac{\partial^2 u}{\partial x^2} + \frac{\partial^2 u}{\partial y^2} + \frac{\partial^2 u}{\partial z^2} = \frac{t}{4\pi} \int\!\!\int_{S_1} \left( \frac{\partial^2 \varphi}{\partial \xi^2} + \frac{\partial^2 \varphi}{\partial \eta^2} + \frac{\partial^2 \varphi}{\partial \zeta^2} \right) d\sigma_1$$

or, returning to the original range of integration,

$$\frac{\partial^2 u}{\partial x^2} + \frac{\partial^2 u}{\partial y^2} + \frac{\partial^2 u}{\partial z^2} = \frac{1}{4\pi a^2 t} \int\!\!\int_{S_{at}} \left( \frac{\partial^2 \varphi}{\partial \xi^2} + \frac{\partial^2 \varphi}{\partial \eta^2} + \frac{\partial^2 \varphi}{\partial \zeta^2} \right) d\sigma_r.$$

$$(11.5)$$

Differentiating (11.4) with respect to $t$, we obtain

$$\frac{\partial u}{\partial t} = \frac{1}{4\pi} \int\!\!\int_{S_1} \varphi(x + \alpha at, y + \beta at, z + \gamma at) \, d\sigma_1 +$$

$$+ \frac{at}{4\pi} \int\!\!\int_{S_1} \left( \alpha \frac{\partial \varphi}{\partial \xi} + \beta \frac{\partial \varphi}{\partial \eta} + \gamma \frac{\partial \varphi}{\partial \zeta} \right) d\sigma_1. \quad (11.6)$$

To evaluate $\partial^2 u/\partial t^2$ let us rewrite (11.6) in the form

$$\frac{\partial u}{\partial t} = \frac{u}{t} + \frac{1}{4\pi at} \iint\limits_{S_{at}} \left( \alpha \frac{\partial \varphi}{\partial \xi} + \beta \frac{\partial \varphi}{\partial \eta} + \gamma \frac{\partial \varphi}{\partial \zeta} \right) d\sigma_r.$$

Using the Gauss theorem formula we obtain

$$\frac{\partial u}{\partial t} = \frac{u}{t} + \frac{1}{4\pi at} \iiint\limits_{D_{at}} \left( \frac{\partial^2 \varphi}{\partial \xi^2} + \frac{\partial^2 \varphi}{\partial \eta^2} + \frac{\partial^2 \varphi}{\partial \zeta^2} \right) d\xi \, d\eta \, d\zeta,$$

where $D_{at}$ is a sphere of radius $r = at$ with centre at the point $M(x, y, z)$. Substituting

$$I = \iiint\limits_{D_{at}} \left( \frac{\partial^2 \varphi}{\partial \xi^2} + \frac{\partial^2 \varphi}{\partial \eta^2} + \frac{\partial^2 \varphi}{\partial \zeta^2} \right) d\xi \, d\eta \, d\zeta,$$

we have

$$\frac{\partial u}{\partial t} = \frac{u}{t} + \frac{I}{4\pi at}.$$

Differentiating this equation with respect to $t$, we obtain

$$\frac{\partial^2 u}{\partial t^2} = -\frac{u}{t^2} + \frac{1}{t}\left( \frac{u}{t} + \frac{I}{4\pi at} \right) -$$

$$-\frac{I}{4\pi at^2} + \frac{1}{4\pi at} \frac{\partial I}{\partial t} = \frac{1}{4\pi at} \frac{dI}{dt}. \tag{11.7}$$

It is readily seen that

$$\frac{\partial I}{\partial t} = a \iint\limits_{S_{at}} \left( \frac{\partial^2 \varphi}{\partial \xi^2} + \frac{\partial^2 \varphi}{\partial \eta^2} + \frac{\partial^2 \varphi}{\partial \zeta^2} \right) d\sigma_r. \tag{11.8}$$

In point of fact, if we transform $I$ to spherical coordinates $(\rho, \theta, \psi)$ with the centre at the point $M(x, y, z)$, we have

$$I = \int\limits_{0}^{at} \int\limits_{0}^{2\pi} \int\limits_{0}^{\pi} \left( \frac{\partial^2 \varphi}{\partial \xi^2} + \frac{\partial^2 \varphi}{\partial \eta^2} + \frac{\partial^2 \varphi}{\partial \zeta^2} \right) \rho^2 \sin\theta \, d\theta \, d\psi \, d\rho.$$

Differentiating with respect to $t$, we obtain

$$\frac{\partial I}{\partial t} = a \int_0^{2\pi} \int_0^{\pi} \left( \frac{\partial^2 \varphi}{\partial \xi^2} + \frac{\partial^2 \varphi}{\partial \eta^2} + \frac{\partial^2 \varphi}{\partial \zeta^2} \right)_{\rho=at} a^2 t^2 \sin \theta \, d\theta \, d\psi =$$

$$= a \int \int_{S_{at}} \left( \frac{\partial^2 \varphi}{\partial \xi^2} + \frac{\partial^2 \varphi}{\partial \eta^2} + \frac{\partial^2 \varphi}{\partial \zeta^2} \right) d\sigma_r.$$

Comparison of (11.5), (11.7), and (11.8) will show that the function $u(x, y, z, t)$ given by (11.3) satisfies the wave equation (11.1) for any $\varphi(x, y, z)$ provided that the latter function has continuous first-order and second-order derivatives. It follows immediately from (11.4) and (11.6) that $u(x, y, z, t)$ satisfies the initial conditions

$$u|_{t=0} = 0, \quad \frac{\partial u}{\partial t}\bigg|_{t=0} = \varphi(x, y, z). \tag{11.9}$$

If $u$ is a solution of the wave equation (11.1) with the initial conditions (11.9), it is easy to see that the function

$$v(x, y, z, t) = \frac{\partial u}{\partial t}$$

is also a solution of (11.1) subject to the initial conditions

$$v|_{t=0} = \varphi(x, y, z),$$

$$\frac{\partial v}{\partial t}\bigg|_{t=0} = \frac{\partial^2 u}{\partial t^2}\bigg|_{t=0} = a^2 \left( \frac{\partial^2 u}{\partial x^2} + \frac{\partial^2 u}{\partial y^2} + \frac{\partial^2 u}{\partial z^2} \right)\bigg|_{t=0} = 0. \tag{11.10}$$

If we denote $\varphi(x, y, z)$ by $\varphi_1(x, y, z)$ in the case of the initial conditions (11.9) and by $\varphi_0(x, y, z)$ in the case of the initial conditions given by (11.10), and if we combine the solutions obtained in this way, we shall obtain a solution of (11.1) which satisfies the initial conditions given by (11.2).

The solution of the wave equation (11.1) subject to initial conditions (11.2) may therefore be written in the form

$$u(x, y, z, t) = \frac{1}{4\pi a} \frac{\partial}{\partial t} \int\int_{S_{at}} \frac{\varphi_0(\xi, \eta, \zeta)}{r} \, d\sigma_r +$$

$$+ \frac{1}{4\pi a} \int\int_{S_{at}} \frac{\varphi_1(\xi, \eta, \zeta)}{r} \, d\sigma_r, \tag{11.11}$$

which is known as Poisson's formula.

In order to obtain a clear physical picture of the propagation of waves in three-dimensional space, as described by Poisson's formula (11.11), let us suppose that the initial disturbance was localised in a finite region $V$ bounded by the surface $S$, i.e. the functions $\varphi_0$ and $\varphi_1$ are both zero outside $V$. Consider a point $M(x, y, z)$ outside $V$, and let $d$ and $D$ represent the minimum and maximum distances of $M$ from the $S$ (fig. 6). When $t < d/a$, the sphere $S_{at}$ lies outside $V$, the two functions $\varphi_0$ and $\varphi_1$ are zero on $S_{at}$, and from (11.11) we have $u(M, t) = 0$, i.e. the initial disturbances have not succeeded in reaching the point $M$. At $t = d/a$, the sphere $S_{at}$ touches the surface $S$ and the leading front of the wave arrives at $M$. Between $t = d/a$ and $t = D/a$ the sphere $S_{at}$ cuts the region $V$ and (11.11) yields $u(M, t) \neq 0$. Finally, for $t > D/a$ the sphere $S_{at}$ will not have common points with $S$ (the entire region $V$ will lie inside the sphere $S_{at}$), and it is evident from (11.11) that $u(M, t) = 0$, i.e. the initial disturbance has passed through the point $M$. The instant $t = D/a$ corresponds to the passage of the trailing edge of the wave through $M$. At a given time $t$ the leading edge of the wave takes the form of a surface which separates points which have not begun to oscillate from those which are already in oscillation. It follows from the foregoing that all points on this surface are at the minimum distance $at$ from $S$. The leading edge is the envelope of the family of spheres with centres on the surface $S$ and radii $at$. The trailing edge of the wave at time $t$ is a surface separating points which are still oscillating from those which no longer oscillate. The constant $a$ is the velocity of propagation of the wave front. We thus see that the initial disturbance, which is localised in space, gives rise at each point $M$ in space to an effect localised in time. Moreover, the waves have both leading and trailing edges (the Huygens principle).

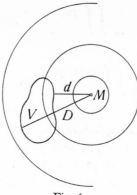

Fig. 6.

## 2. Cylindrical waves.

Consider the special case when the functions $\varphi_0$ and $\varphi_1$ depend only on $x$ and $y$, i.e. they retain a constant value along any line parallel to the $z$-axis. If we displace the point $M(x, y, z)$ parallel to the $z$-axis, the first part of Poisson's formula (11.11) will remain constant, i.e. the function $u$ will also be independent of $z$, and (11.11) will be the solution of

$$\frac{\partial^2 u}{\partial t^2} = a^2 \left( \frac{\partial^2 u}{\partial x^2} + \frac{\partial^2 u}{\partial y^2} \right) \tag{11.12}$$

subject to the initial conditions

$$u|_{t=0} = \varphi_0(x, y), \quad \frac{\partial u}{\partial t}\bigg|_{t=0} = \varphi_1(x, y). \tag{11.13}$$

We can consider (11.11) by remaining exclusively on the $x$, $y$-plane. To do this, the integrals in (11.11) which are taken over spheres must be transformed into integrals over circles on the $x$, $y$-plane. Consider a point $M(x, y)$ on the $x$, $y$-plane. Points with coordinates $(\xi, \eta, \zeta)$ which are given by

$$\xi = x + \alpha at, \quad \eta = y + \beta at, \quad \zeta = z + \gamma at$$

and $z = 0$ are variable points on a sphere $S_{at}$ with centre at $M(x, y, 0)$ and radius $at$. Parts of this sphere which lie below and above the $x$, $y$-plane project on to the $x$, $y$-plane as the circle $C_{at}$

with centre $M(x, y)$ and radius $at$. Since

$$dC_{at} = \cos(nz)\,d\sigma_{at},$$

where $n$ represents the direction of the normal to $S_{at}$, i.e. the direction of the radius of the sphere forming an acute angle with the $z$-axis. If $N$ is a variable point on the sphere and $N_1$ is its projection on the $x, y$-plane, then

$$\cos(nz) = \frac{|NN_1|}{|MN|} = \frac{\sqrt{a^2t^2 - (\xi - x)^2 - (\eta - y)^2}}{at},$$

where $(\xi, \eta)$ are the coordinates of a variable point on the circle $C_{at}$. On transforming (11.11) we obtain

$$u(x, y, t) = \frac{1}{2\pi a} \frac{\partial}{\partial t} \iint\limits_{C_{at}} \frac{\varphi_0(\xi, \eta)\,d\xi\,d\eta}{\sqrt{a^2t^2 - (\xi - x)^2 - (\eta - y)^2}} +$$

$$+ \frac{1}{2\pi a} \iint\limits_{C_{at}} \frac{\varphi_1(\xi, \eta)\,d\xi\,d\eta}{\sqrt{a^2t^2 - (\xi - x)^2 - (\eta - y)^2}}. \qquad (11.14)$$

which is the solution of (11.12) subject to the initial conditions given by (11.13).

Let us suppose that the initial disturbance is limited to a finite region $B$ on the $x, y$-plane bounded by the contour $l$, i.e. $\varphi_0(x, y)$ and $\varphi_1(x, y)$ both vanish outside $B$, and that the point $M(x, y)$ lies outside the region $B$. For times $t < d/a$, where $d$ is the minimum distance of $M$ from the contour $l$, the circle $C_{at}$ does not have common points with $B$, the functions $\varphi_0(x, y)$ and $\varphi_1(x, y)$ are both zero on $C_{at}$, and equation (11.14) gives $u(x, y, t) = 0$, which means that the disturbance has not reached $M$. The leading edge of the wave arrives at $M$ at time $t = d/a$. If $D$ is the maximum distance of $M$ from the contour $l$, the circle $C_{at}$ will contain the entire region $B$ when $t > D/a$, and we obtain

$$u(x, y, t) = \frac{1}{2\pi a} \frac{\partial}{\partial t} \iint\limits_{B} \frac{\varphi_0(\xi, \eta)\,d\xi\,d\eta}{\sqrt{a^2t^2 - (\xi - x)^2 - (\eta - y)^2}} +$$

$$+ \frac{1}{2\pi a} \iint\limits_{B} \frac{\varphi_1(\xi, \eta)\,d\xi\,d\eta}{\sqrt{a^2t^2 - (\xi - x)^2 - (\eta - y)^2}}. \qquad (11.15)$$

For $t > D/a$, the function $u(x, y, t)$ will not be zero as in the three-dimensional case. However, in view of the presence of $a^2t^2$ in the denominator, we can see that $u(x, y, t) \to 0$ as $t \to \infty$. It follows that the initial disturbance which is localised on the plane is not localised in time. In this case we have a wave which has a leading edge but no trailing edge (the Huygens principle does not apply). In three-dimensional space (11.12) corresponds to the so-called *cylindrical waves*.

**3. Continuous dependence of solutions on initial conditions.** All the formulae which we have derived are solutions of Cauchy's problem for the wave equation, and contain integrals of the initial functions multiplied by definite functions and time-derivatives of such integrals. Therefore, if we vary the initial functions $\varphi_0$ and $\varphi_1$ so that they and their first derivatives undergo small changes, the function $u$ which is the solution of Cauchy's problem will also undergo a small change, i.e. we have a *continuous dependence of the solution on the initial data*. We are, of course, assuming that $t$ is finite if the domain in which the initial functions are specified is infinite.

**4. Uniqueness theorem.** We shall now prove the uniqueness of the solution of Cauchy's problem for the wave equation. We shall assume for the sake of simplicity that $a = 1$, which may be achieved by replacing $t$ in the wave equation by $t/a$. Consider the case of three independent variables

$$\frac{\partial^2 u}{\partial t^2} = \frac{\partial^2 u}{\partial x^2} + \frac{\partial^2 u}{\partial y^2}, \tag{11.16}$$

$$u|_{t=0} = \varphi_0(x, y), \quad \frac{\partial u}{\partial t}\bigg|_{t=0} = \varphi_1(x, y). \tag{11.17}$$

We shall show that Cauchy's problem specified by (11.16) and (11.17) has a unique solution in a class of twice continuously differentiable functions. Suppose that $u_1(x, y, t)$ and $u_2(x, y, t)$ satisfy equation (11.16) subject to the initial conditions (11.17). The difference $u(x, y, t) = u_1(x, y, t) - u_2(x, y, t)$ will then satisfy the wave equation (11.16) and the initial conditions

$$u|_{t=0} = 0, \quad \frac{\partial u}{\partial t}\bigg|_{t=0} = 0. \tag{11.18}$$

We shall show that $u \equiv 0$ for any $x, y$ and any $t > 0$. Consider the three-dimensional space $(x, y, t)$ and an arbitrary point $M(x_0, y_0, t_0)$ where $t_0 > 0$. With this point as the apex, let us draw the cone

$$(t - t_0)^2 - (x - x_0)^2 - (y - y_0)^2$$

until it cuts the plane $t = 0$. We shall refer to this cone as the characteristic cone.* Suppose that $D$ is a domain bounded by the lateral surface of the characteristic cone and that part of the plane $t = 0$ which lies inside the cone.
It is quite easy to verify that

$$2 \frac{\partial u}{\partial t} \left( \frac{\partial^2 u}{\partial t^2} - \frac{\partial^2 u}{\partial x^2} - \frac{\partial^2 u}{\partial y^2} \right) =$$

$$= \frac{\partial}{\partial t} \left[ \left( \frac{\partial u}{\partial x} \right)^2 + \left( \frac{\partial u}{\partial y} \right)^2 + \left( \frac{\partial u}{\partial t} \right)^2 \right] -$$

$$- 2 \frac{\partial}{\partial x} \left( \frac{\partial u}{\partial t} \frac{\partial u}{\partial x} \right) - 2 \frac{\partial}{\partial y} \left( \frac{\partial u}{\partial t} \frac{\partial u}{\partial y} \right).$$

Let us integrate this identity over the domain $D$. The integral on the left vanishes, because $u$ is a solution of (11.16):

$$0 = \iiint_D \left\{ \frac{\partial}{\partial t} \left[ \left( \frac{\partial u}{\partial x} \right)^2 + \left( \frac{\partial u}{\partial y} \right)^2 + \left( \frac{\partial u}{\partial t} \right)^2 \right] - \right.$$

$$\left. - 2 \frac{\partial}{\partial x} \left( \frac{\partial u}{\partial t} \frac{\partial u}{\partial x} \right) - 2 \frac{\partial}{\partial y} \left( \frac{\partial u}{\partial t} \frac{\partial u}{\partial y} \right) \right\} dx \, dy \, dt.$$

We can now transform this integral, using the Gauss theorem. Let $\Gamma$ be the lateral surface of the cone and $\sigma_0$ its base. Since on $\sigma_0$ the initial conditions (11.18) ensure that

$$\frac{\partial u}{\partial x} = \frac{\partial u}{\partial y} = \frac{\partial u}{\partial t} = 0,$$

---

* For further details see § 12.

we are left with the integral

$$\iint\limits_{\Gamma} \left\{ \left[ \left( \frac{\partial u}{\partial x} \right)^2 + \left( \frac{\partial u}{\partial y} \right)^2 + \left( \frac{\partial t}{\partial u} \right)^2 \right] \cos (nt) - \right.$$

$$\left. - 2 \frac{\partial u}{\partial t} \frac{\partial u}{\partial x} \cos (nx) - 2 \frac{\partial u}{\partial t} \frac{\partial u}{\partial y} \cos (ny) \, dS = 0. \right. \qquad (11.19)$$

On the lateral surface $\Gamma$ of the characteristic cone we have

$$\cos^2 (nt) - \cos^2 (nx) - \cos^2 (ny) = 0.$$

Equation (11.19) may now be rewritten in the form

$$\iint\limits_{\Gamma} \frac{1}{\cos (nt)} \left\{ \left[ \frac{\partial u}{\partial x} \cos (nt) - \frac{\partial u}{\partial t} \cos (nx) \right]^2 + \right.$$

$$\left. + \left[ \frac{\partial u}{\partial y} \cos (nt) - \frac{\partial u}{\partial t} \cos (ny) \right]^2 \right\} dS = 0. \qquad (11.20)$$

On $\Gamma$ we have $\cos (nt) = 1/\sqrt{2}$, and since the integrand is continuous and non-negative, it follows from (11.20) that it vanishes on the surface of the cone, i.e.

$$\frac{\partial u}{\partial x} \cos (nt) - \frac{\partial u}{\partial t} \cos (nx) = 0, \quad \frac{\partial u}{\partial y} \cos (nt) - \frac{\partial u}{\partial t} \cos (ny) = 0$$

$$(\text{on } \Gamma)$$

or

$$\frac{\dfrac{\partial u}{\partial x}}{\cos (nx)} = \frac{\dfrac{\partial u}{\partial y}}{\cos (ny)} = \frac{\dfrac{\partial u}{\partial t}}{\cos (nt)} = \lambda. \qquad (11.21)$$

Let $l$ represent the direction of a generator of the characteristic cone. Using (11.21) we have

$$\frac{\partial u}{\partial l} = \frac{\partial u}{\partial x} \cos (lx) + \frac{\partial u}{\partial y} \cos (ly) + \frac{\partial u}{\partial t} \cos (lt) =$$

$$= \lambda [\cos (nx) \cos (lx) + \cos (ny) \cos (ly) + \cos (nt) \cos (lt)] =$$

$$= \lambda \cos (nl) = 0,$$

since a generator of the cone is always perpendicular to the normal to its surface. It follows that $u = $ const along the generator $l$. At the point where the generator cuts the plane $t = 0$ we have $u = 0$, and therefore $u = 0$ along the generator. In particular, this is so at the apex of the cone, i.e. $u(M) = 0$, which was to be proved. This result remains valid if the homogeneous initial conditions given by (11.18) hold not on the entire $x, y$-plane but only on the base $\sigma_0$ of the domain $D$. Hence it may be concluded that the magnitude of the solution of the wave equation (11.16) at the point $M(x_0, y_0, t_0)$ depends only on the initial values on that part of the $t = 0$ plane which is cut on this plane by the characteristic cone with apex at $M(x_0, y_0, t_0)$.

## 5. Inhomogeneous wave equation. Consider the equation

$$\frac{\partial^2 u}{\partial t^2} = a^2 \left( \frac{\partial^2 u}{\partial x^2} + \frac{\partial^2 u}{\partial y^2} + \frac{\partial^2 u}{\partial z^2} \right) + f(x, y, z, t). \tag{11.22}$$

We shall seek its solution subject to the initial conditions

$$u|_{t=0} = 0, \quad \frac{\partial u}{\partial t}\bigg|_{t=0} = 0. \tag{11.23}$$

By adding to this the solution of the homogeneous equation subject to the initial conditions (11.2), we shall obtain the solution of (11.22) subject to (11.2).

In order to solve the problem specified by (11.22) and (11.23), consider the homogeneous equations

$$\frac{\partial^2 v}{\partial t^2} = a^2 \left( \frac{\partial^2 v}{\partial x^2} + \frac{\partial^2 v}{\partial y^2} + \frac{\partial^2 v}{\partial z^2} \right), \tag{11.24}$$

subject to the initial conditions

$$v|_{t=\tau} = 0, \quad \frac{\partial v}{\partial t}\bigg|_{t=\tau} = f(x, y, z, \tau), \tag{11.25}$$

Here, the initial instant of time is not $t = 0$ but $t = \tau$, where $\tau$ is a parameter. The solution of the problem specified by (11.24) and (11.25) will be expressed by Poisson's formula with $t$ replaced by $t - \tau$, since the initial instant of time is not $t = 0$ but $t = \tau$. We thus have

$$v(x, y, z, t; \tau) = \frac{t - \tau}{4\pi} \iint\limits_{S_1} f[x + \alpha a(t - \tau), \qquad (11.26)$$

$$y + \beta a(t - \tau), \ z + \gamma a(t - \tau), \tau] d\sigma_1.$$

We shall show that the function

$$u(x, y, z, t) = \int_0^t v(x, y, z, t; \tau) d\tau, \qquad (11.27)$$

is a solution of the non-homogeneous wave equation (11.22) subject to the initial conditions given by (11.23).

In point of fact, from (11.27) we have

$$\Delta u = \int_0^t \Delta v(x, y, z, t; \tau) d\tau. \qquad (11.28)$$

Differentiating (11.27) with respect to $t$, we obtain

$$\frac{\partial u}{\partial t} = \int_0^t \frac{\partial v}{\partial t} d\tau + v(x, y, z, t; \tau) \bigg|_{\tau = t}. \qquad (11.29)$$

The term outside the integral sign is zero, in view of the first of the two conditions in (11.25). Differentiating once again with respect to $t$, we have

$$\frac{\partial^2 u}{\partial t^2} = \int_0^t \frac{\partial^2 v}{\partial t^2} d\tau + \frac{\partial v(x, y, z, t; \tau)}{\partial t} \bigg|_{\tau = t},$$

where, in view of the second condition in (11.25), the second term on the right is equal to $f(x, y, z, t)$, i.e.

$$\frac{\partial^2 u}{\partial t^2} = \int_0^t \frac{\partial^2 v}{\partial t^2} dt + f(x, y, z, t). \qquad (11.30)$$

It follows directly from (11.28), (11.30), and (11.24) that the function $u(x, y, z, t)$ defined by (11.27) satisfies the non-homogeneous equation (11.22). The initial conditions given by (11.23) are also satisfied, which follows from (11.27) and (11.29). If we now substitute (11.26) into (11.27) we obtain

$$u(x, y, z, t) = \frac{1}{4\pi} \int\limits_0^t (t - \tau) \left\{ \iint\limits_{S_1} f[x + \alpha a(t - \tau), \right.$$

$$\left. y + \beta a(t - \tau), z + \gamma a(t - \tau); \tau] d\sigma_1 \right\} d\tau.$$

Let us replace $\tau$ by the new integration variable $r = a(t - \tau)$, so that

$$u(x, y, z, t) =$$

$$= \frac{1}{4\pi a^2} \int\limits_0^{at} \int\limits_0^{2\pi} \int\limits_0^{\pi} \frac{f\left(x + \alpha r, y + \beta r, z + \gamma r, t - \dfrac{r}{a}\right)}{r} r^2 \sin\theta \, d\theta \, d\psi \, dr.$$

Finally, replacing spherical coordinates by the rectangular coordinates

$$\xi = x + \alpha r, \quad \eta = y + \beta r, \quad \zeta = z + \gamma r$$

and recalling that $\alpha^2 + \beta^2 + \gamma^2 = 1$, we obtain

$$r = \sqrt{(x - \xi)^2 + (y - \eta)^2 + (z - \zeta)^2},$$

The expression for $u(x, y, z, t)$ now becomes

$$u(x, y, z, t) = \frac{1}{4\pi a^2} \iiint\limits_{D_{at}} \frac{f\left(\xi, \eta, \zeta, t - \dfrac{r}{a}\right)}{r} d\xi \, d\eta \, d\zeta, \qquad (11.31)$$

where $D_{at}$ is a sphere of radius $at$ centred on the point $(x, y, z)$. This is the so-called *retarded potential*.

We note that in evaluating the integral, the function $f$ is taken not at the time $t$ but at a preceding time $t = r/a$, the delay being just equal to the time necessary for a process propagating with velocity $a$ to traverse the path between $(\xi, \eta, \zeta)$ and $(x, y, z)$.

The solution of the non-homogeneous equation

$$\frac{\partial^2 u}{\partial t^2} = a^2 \left( \frac{\partial^2 u}{\partial x^2} + \frac{\partial^2 u}{\partial y^2} \right) + f(x, y, t), \qquad (11.32)$$

subject to the initial conditions

$$u|_{t=0} = 0, \quad \frac{\partial u}{\partial t}\bigg|_{t=0} = 0. \tag{11.33}$$

can be obtained in a similar way. The final result is

$$u(x, y, t) = \frac{1}{2\pi a} \int\limits_0^t \left[ \iint\limits_{\rho \leqslant a(t-\tau)} \frac{f(\xi, \eta, \tau)}{\sqrt{a^2(t-\tau)^2 - \rho^2}} \, d\xi \, d\eta \right] d\tau, \tag{11.34}$$

where

$$\rho^2 = (x - \xi)^2 + (y - \eta)^2.$$

In the case of the equation

$$\frac{\partial^2 u}{\partial t^2} = a^2 \frac{\partial^2 u}{\partial x^2} + f(x, t), \tag{11.35}$$

the solution satisfying the initial conditions given by (11.23) is

$$u(x, t) = \frac{1}{2a} \int\limits_0^t \left[ \int\limits_{x-a(t-\tau)}^{x+a(t-\tau)} f(\xi, \tau) \, d\xi \right] d\tau. \tag{11.36}$$

**6. Point source.** If we suppose that the free term in equation (11.22) is different from zero only in a small sphere centred on the origin, then as the radius of the sphere tends to zero, and the intensity of the external force increases without limit, we can obtain in the limit the solution of the wave equation for a point source which begins to act at time $t = 0$ and can be an arbitrary function of time. Let us suppose that

$$f(x, y, z, t) = 0 \quad \text{when} \quad \sqrt{x^2 + y^2 + z^2} \geqslant \varepsilon \tag{11.37}$$

and

$$\iiint\limits_{D_\varepsilon} f(x, y, z, t) \, dx \, dy \, dz = 4\pi a^2 \omega(t), \tag{11.38}$$

where $D_\varepsilon$ is a sphere of radius $\varepsilon$ centred on the origin.

Consider now (11.31) with $at < \sqrt{x^2 + y^2 + z^2}$. In view of (11.37) it is sufficient to integrate over the sphere $D_\varepsilon$. When $\varepsilon \to 0$ the quantity $r$ will be equal to the distance of the point $(x, y, z)$ from the origin, i.e. $r = \sqrt{x^2 + y^2 + z^2}$, and bearing in mind (11.38) we obtain

$$u(x, y, z, t) = \frac{1}{r} \omega \left( t - \frac{r}{a} \right) \qquad (at > r). \tag{11.39}$$

When $r > at$ it is clear that $u(x, y, z, t) = 0$, since for $r < at$ the region of integration in (11.31) does not contain the sphere $D_\varepsilon$ for small enough $\varepsilon$. We note that the function given by (11.39) satisfies the homogeneous wave equation (11.1) for any $\omega(t)$ and represents a spherical wave propagating radially from the origin with a velocity $a$.

In the case of equation (11.32) we must suppose as above that

$$f(x, y, t) = 0 \quad \text{when} \quad \sqrt{x^2 + y^2} \geqslant \varepsilon,$$

$$\iint\limits_{C_\varepsilon} f(x, y, t)\, dx\, dy = 2\pi a \omega(t),$$

where $C_\varepsilon$ is a circle of radius $\varepsilon$ centred on the origin.

Returning now to (11.34), and passing to the limit as $\varepsilon \to 0$, we obtain the solution for a point source in the case of cylindrical waves:

$$u(x, y, t) = \int\limits_0^{t-(\rho/a)} \frac{\omega(\tau)\, d\tau}{\sqrt{a^2(t - \tau)^2 - \rho^2}} \qquad (at > \rho), \tag{11.40}$$

$$u(x, y, t) = 0 \quad \text{when} \quad at < \rho \qquad (\rho = \sqrt{x^2 + y^2}).$$

We note that the effect of a point source at a point $(x, y, z)$ at time $t$ depends only on the intensity of the source at time $t - \rho/a$. In the case of equation (11.40), on the other hand, this effect is determined by the effect of the point source during the time interval between $t = 0$ and $t - \rho/a$.

## § 12. Cauchy's problem: characteristics

Consider the hyperbolic equation

$$\sum_{i,k=1}^{n} a_{ik}(x_1, \ldots, x_n) \frac{\partial^2 u}{\partial x_i \partial x_k} +$$

$$+ F\left( x_1, \ldots, x_n, u, \frac{\partial u}{\partial x_1}, \ldots, \frac{\partial u}{\partial x_n} \right) = 0, \tag{12.1}$$

where $a_{ik} = a_{ki}$. The functions $a_{ik}$ are real and are defined in a domain $D$ of the space $(x_1, \ldots, x_n)$.

Suppose that we are given in the domain $D$ a smooth $(n-1)$-dimensional surface $S$ and a line $l$ through each point on $S$ which is not tangent to $S$ and varies smoothly along this surface, for example the normal to the surface.

We shall specify the values of the function $u(x_1, \ldots, x_n)$ on the surface $S$, and its first-order derivatives along the line $l$. We shall refer to these values on $S$ as the initial Cauchy data.

Cauchy's problem for equation (12.1) can be formulated as follows: *determine the solution of equation* (12.1) *in the neighbourhood of the surface $S$ which satisfies the initial Cauchy data on $S$.*

The initial Cauchy data determine the function $u(x_1, \ldots, x_n)$ and its first-order partial derivatives on $S$.

Consider the following problem: is it possible with the aid of the differential equation (12.1), and the initial Cauchy data to determine uniquely on $S$ the second-order and higher-order derivatives of the $u(x_1, \ldots, x_n)$?* We shall begin with the case where the initial conditions have the special form

$$u|_{x_1=x_1^0} = \varphi_0(x_2, \ldots, x_n), \quad \frac{\partial u}{\partial x_1}\bigg|_{x_1=x_1^0} = \varphi_1(x_2, \ldots, x_n), \quad (12.2)$$

i.e. the initial data are given on the hyperplane $x_1 = x_1^0$ and $l$ is chosen to be the normal. The initial data (12.2) enable us to determine on the hyperplane $x_1 = x_1^0$ all the first-order and all the second-order derivatives except for $\partial^2 u/\partial x_1^2$. In order to determine the latter, we must use equation (12.1) with $x_1 = x_1^0$. There are then two possibilities

$$\text{I. } a_{11}(x_1^0, x_2, \ldots, x_n) \neq 0, \quad \text{II. } a_n(x_1^0, x_2, \ldots, x_n) = 0.$$

In Case I we can unambiguously determine the derivative $\partial^2 u/\partial x^2$ on the hyperplane $x = x_1^0$ and the higher-order derivatives.

In Case II we shall arrive either at an impossible equation or at an identity, i.e. we shall have either incompatibility or indeterminacy when we try to find the second derivatives on the hyperplane $x_1 = x_1^0$.

---

\* We are assuming that the solution $u(x_1, \ldots, x_n)$ of (12.1) exists.

Now consider the general case when the initial Cauchy data are given on a plane $S$:

$$\omega_1(x_1, \ldots, x_n) = 0. \tag{12.3}$$

Let us introduce the new coordinates $\xi_1, \ldots, \xi_n$ in the vicinity of $S$ such that

$$\xi_i = \omega_i(x_1, \ldots, x_n) \qquad (i = 1, 2, \ldots, n), \tag{12.4}$$

where the functions $\omega_i(x_1, \ldots, x_n)$ $(i = 2, 3, \ldots, n)$ are chosen so that the transformation Jacobian does not vanish on $S$.

The derivatives with respect to the old variables can now be expressed in terms of the new variables as follows:

$$\frac{\partial u}{\partial x_i} = \sum_{l=1}^{n} \frac{\partial u}{\partial \xi_l} \frac{\partial \omega_l}{\partial x_i},$$

$$\frac{\partial^2 u}{\partial x_i \partial x_k} = \sum_{l,j=1}^{n} \frac{\partial^2 u}{\partial \xi_l \partial \xi_j} \frac{\partial \omega_l}{\partial x_i} \frac{\partial \omega_j}{\partial x_k} + \sum_{l=1}^{n} \frac{\partial u}{\partial x_l} \frac{\partial^2 \omega_l}{\partial x_i \partial x_k}.$$

Substituting into (12.1), we have

$$\bar{a}_{11} \frac{\partial^2 u}{\partial \xi_1^2} + \ldots = 0, \tag{12.5}$$

where

$$\bar{a}_{11} = \sum_{i,k=1}^{n} a_{ik} \frac{\partial \omega_1}{\partial x_i} \frac{\partial \omega_1}{\partial x_k}. \tag{12.6}$$

The terms which are not written out in full do not contain $\partial^2 u / \partial \xi_1^2$. In view of (12.3) and (12.4), the initial data for the transformed equation (12.5) are given on the hyperplane $\xi_1 = 0$, i.e. they have the special form indicated above. Therefore, in this case we can use the results obtained at the beginning of this section, but only for the new independent variables. In view of (12.6), we may conclude that for the initial Cauchy data on the surface (12.3) to lead to an incompatibility or an indeterminacy in the second-order derivatives on $S$, it is necessary and sufficient that the function $\omega_1(x_1, \ldots, x_n)$ shall satisfy the condition

$$\sum_{i,k=1}^{n} a_{ik} \frac{\partial \omega_1}{\partial x_i} \frac{\partial \omega_1}{\partial x_k} = 0, \tag{12.7}$$

Moreover, this condition should be satisfied for $\omega_1 = 0$, i.e. when (12.3) holds.

The surface $\omega_1(x_1, \ldots, x_n) = 0$ is called the *characteristic surface* of equation (12.1), or simply the *characteristic*, if equation (12.7) holds at each point on this surface.

We must emphasise that although (12.7) has the external form of a first-order partial differential equation in $\omega_1$, this is not so by definition. In point of fact, the condition given by (12.7) should not be satisfied identically with respect to $(x_1, \ldots, x_n)$, but only when $\omega_1(x_1, \ldots, x_n) = 0$, i.e. at each point on the characteristic surface. We shall now require (12.7) to be satisfied identically with respect to $(x_1, \ldots, x_n)$. The condition given by (12.6) will then represent the usual first-order partial differential equation, and any of its solutions which are not constants will give not one but a whole *family of characteristics*:

$$\omega_1(x_1, \ldots, x_n) = C, \tag{12.8}$$

where $C$ is an arbitrary constant.

Conversely, for equation (12.8) to define a family of characteristics for an arbitrary constant $C$ it is necessary and sufficient that $\omega_1(x_1, \ldots, x_n)$ shall satisfy (12.7). It may be shown that any characteristic of (12.1) may be included in the family (12.8), and that in this way the solutions of (12.7) will yield all the characteristics.

Equation (12.7) is called the *equation of characteristics* for equation (12.1).

**Example.** Consider the wave equation

$$\frac{\partial^2 u}{\partial t^2} - \frac{\partial^2 u}{\partial x^2} - \frac{\partial^2 u}{\partial y^2} = 0 \tag{12.9}$$

and the cone

$$\kappa = t^2 - x^2 - y^2.$$

Equation (12.7) is of the form

$$\left(\frac{\partial \omega}{\partial t}\right)^2 - \left(\frac{\partial \omega}{\partial x}\right)^2 - \left(\frac{\partial \omega}{\partial y}\right)^2 = 0. \tag{12.10}$$

and is satisfied for $\omega = \kappa = 0$, since

$$4t^2 - 4x^2 - 4y^2 = 4(t^2 - x^2 - y^2) = 4\kappa = 0.$$

It follows that the cone $\kappa = 0$ is a characteristic surface of equation (12.9), while the surfaces $\kappa = C$ when $C \neq 0$ are not characteristic surfaces. The cone $\kappa = 0$ may be included in the family of cones

$$\omega_1 = t - \sqrt{x^2 + y^2} = C,$$

where $\omega_1$ satisfies (12.10). All the surfaces in the family $\omega_1 = C$ are characteristic surfaces of equation (12.9).

If the surface $S$ ($\omega_1 = 0$) is such that (12.7) is not satisfied, over the entire surface $S$,* then the second derivatives of the required function $u$ are unambiguously defined on $S$. It then follows from the above discussion that by introducing the change of variables given by (12.4), we can rewrite (12.5) in the form

$$\frac{\partial^2 u}{\partial \xi_1^2} = \sum_{i,k=2}^{n} b_{ik} \frac{\partial^2 u}{\partial \xi_i \partial \xi_k} + \sum_{i=1}^{n} b_{1i} \frac{\partial^2 u}{\partial \xi_1 \partial \xi_i} + \ldots, \tag{12.11}$$

and the surface $S$ will then become the hyperplane $\xi_1 = 0$.

This provides us with a means of transforming Cauchy's problem with initial data given on the surface $S$ to a Cauchy problem with initial data on the hyperplane $\xi_1 = 0$. If the plane $S$ is a characteristic, then the function $u(x_1, \ldots, x_n)$ and its first-order partial derivatives must be related on $S$. In point of fact $u(x_1, \ldots, x_n)$ and its partial derivatives on $S$ can be expressed in terms of the corresponding quantities on the plane $\xi_1 = 0$ and vice versa. Suppose that

$$u|_{\xi_1=0} = \bar{\varphi}_0(\xi_2, \ldots, \xi_n), \qquad \frac{\partial u}{\partial \xi_1}\bigg|_{\xi_1=0} = \bar{\varphi}_1(\xi_2, \ldots, \xi_n).$$

If $S$ is the characteristic surface of equation (12.1), then in the transformed equation (12.5) we have $\bar{a}_{11} = 0$ when $\xi_1 = 0$, and

$$\sum_{i,k=2}^{n} \bar{a}_{ik} \frac{\partial^2 u}{\partial \xi_i \partial \xi_k} + 2 \sum_{k=2}^{n} \bar{a}_{1k} \frac{\partial^2 u}{\partial \xi_1 \partial \xi_k} + \ldots = 0 \text{ when } \xi_1 = 0,$$

---

* Since the coefficients $a_{ik}$ and the derivatives $\partial \omega_1/\partial x_i$ are continuous, equation (12.7) will not be satisfied in the vicinity of the surface $S$ in the space $(x_1, \ldots, x_n)$.

where the terms which are not written out in full do not contain first-order derivatives. We thus obtain the following relationship between the functions $\bar{\varphi}_0$ and $\bar{\varphi}_1$:

$$\sum_{i,k=2}^{n} \bar{a}_{ik} \frac{\partial^2 \varphi_0}{\partial \xi_i \partial \xi_k} + 2 \sum_{k=2}^{n} \bar{a}_{1k} \frac{\partial \varphi_1}{\partial \xi_k} + \ldots = 0 \text{ when } \xi_1 = 0.$$

The initial Cauchy data cannot, therefore, be prescribed arbitrarily on the characteristic surface $S$.

It is easy to show that the characteristic surfaces are the only surfaces on which the second derivatives of the solution $u$ of equation (12.1) may possess a discontinuity of the first kind, although the solution itself and its first derivatives remain continuous. In fact, suppose that a solution $u(x_1, \ldots, x_n)$ of equation (12.1) has on the surface

$$\varphi(x_1, \ldots, x_n) = 0 \qquad\qquad\qquad (12.12)$$

a discontinuity of the first kind for second-order derivatives, although the solution itself and its first-order derivatives remain continuous on (12.12). We shall regard this solution $u$ on either side of (12.12) as two different solutions of (12.1). These solutions have on this surface the same Cauchy data but different second-order derivatives, and we may therefore conclude the surface (12.12) to be a characteristic surface of equation (12.1). We shall arrive at the same result if we assume that not only the solution $u$ itself and its first-order partial derivatives, but also the second-order partial derivatives, remain continuous across the surface (12.12), whilst the discontinuity occurs only for derivatives of order higher than 2.

In general, the solution of the second-order equation (12.1) has a *weak discontinuity* on (12.12) if, on passing through the surface, the solution $u(x_1, \ldots, x_n)$ and its first derivatives remain continuous, whereas some derivatives of order higher than 1 have a discontinuity of the first kind on the surface (12.12).

It follows from the above discussion that the surface of a weak discontinuity can only be a characteristic surface.

## § 13. The mixed problem

**1. Formulation of the problem.** Consider the equation

$$\frac{\partial^2 u}{\partial t^2} - \sum_{i,j=1}^{n} a_{ij}(X, t) \frac{\partial^2 u}{\partial x_i \partial x_j} +$$

$$+ \sum_{i=1}^{n} b_i(X, t) \frac{\partial u}{\partial x_i} + c(X, t)u = f(X, t), \tag{13.1}$$

where $a_{ij}$, $b_i$, $c$ and $f$ are given functions in the cylinder $Q_T = \Omega = t(0 < t < T)$, where $\Omega$ is a finite domain of the variables $(x_1, \ldots, x_n) = X$ and $a_{ij} = a_{ji}$. Suppose that in $\bar{Q}_T$ we have

$$\sum_{i,j=1}^{n} a_{ij}(X, t)\xi_i\xi_j \geqslant \alpha \sum_{i=1}^{n} \xi_i^2, \qquad \alpha = \text{const} > 0. \tag{13.2}$$

This condition represents the fact that equation (13.1) is of the *hyperbolic type* in $\bar{Q}_T$.

Consider the following problem: determine in cylinder $Q_T$ the solution of equation (13.1) which satisfies the initial conditions

$$u|_{t=0} = \varphi_0(X), \qquad \frac{\partial u}{\partial t}\bigg|_{t=0} = \varphi_1(X) \tag{13.3}$$

and one of the boundary conditions

$$u|_S = \kappa(P, t) \quad \text{when } t \in [0, T] \tag{13.4}$$

$$\left[ \sum_{i,j=1}^{n} a_{ij}(X, t) \frac{\partial u}{\partial x_i} \cos(nx_j) + hu \right]_S = g(P, t) \quad \text{when } t \in [0, T], \tag{13.5}$$

where $S$ is the boundary of $\Omega$, $P$ is a point on $S$, $n$ is a normal to $S$, $\kappa(P, t)$ and $g(P, t)$ are given functions and $h$ is a given function on $S$.

The problem of finding the solution of (13.1) in the cylinder $Q_T$ subject to the initial conditions (13.3) and one of the boundary conditions (13.4) or (13.5) is called a *mixed problem*.

**2. Uniqueness of the solution of the mixed problem.** For simplicity we shall confine our attention to the equation

$$\rho(x) \frac{\partial^2 u}{\partial t^2} - \frac{\partial}{\partial x}\left(p(x) \frac{\partial u}{\partial x}\right) + q(x)u = f(x, t), \tag{13.6}$$

where $\rho(x)$, $p(x)$, $p'(x)$ and $q(x)$ are continuous functions for $0 \leqslant x \leqslant 1$ where $\rho(x) > \rho_0 > 0$, $p(x) > p_0 > 0$, $q(x) \geqslant 0$.

Consider the following mixed problem for equation (13.6): find the solution of (13.6) in the rectangle $Q[0 < x < 1, 0 < t < T]$ which satisfies the initial conditions

$$u|_{t=0} = \varphi_0(x), \quad \frac{\partial u}{\partial t}\bigg|_{t=0} = \varphi_1(x) \qquad (0 \leqslant x \leqslant l) \tag{13.7}$$

and the boundary conditions

$$u|_{x=0} = \kappa_1(t), \quad u|_{x=l} = \kappa_2(t) \qquad (0 \leqslant t \leqslant T), \tag{13.8}$$

where

$$\varphi_0(0) = \kappa_1(0), \quad \varphi_0(l) = \kappa_2(0), \quad \varphi_1(0) = \kappa'_1(0), \quad \varphi_1(l) = \kappa'_2(0).$$

We shall prove the uniqueness of the solution of the problem specified by (13.6)–(13.8) in a class of twice continuously differentiable functions in the rectangle $Q$. Let us suppose that there are two solutions $u_1(x, t)$ and $u_2(x, t)$ of the mixed problem (13.6)–(13.8). The difference $\omega(x, t) = u_1(x, t) - u_2(x, t)$ will satisfy the homogeneous equation

$$\rho(x) \frac{\partial^2 \omega}{\partial t^2} - \frac{\partial}{\partial x}\left(p(x) \frac{\partial \omega}{\partial x}\right) + q(x)\omega = 0, \tag{13.9}$$

with the initial conditions

$$\omega|_{t=0} = 0, \quad \frac{\partial \omega}{\partial t}\bigg|_{t=0} = 0 \tag{13.10}$$

and the homogeneous boundary conditions

$$\omega|_{x=0} = 0, \quad \omega|_{x=l} = 0. \tag{13.11}$$

We shall show that $\omega(x, t) \equiv 0$ in $\bar{Q}$.

Consider the energy integral

$$E(t) = \tfrac{1}{2} \int\limits_0^l \left[\rho(x)\left(\frac{\partial \omega}{\partial t}\right)^2 + p(x)\left(\frac{\partial \omega}{\partial x}\right)^2 + q(x)\omega^2\right] dx. \tag{13.12}$$

In view of the initial conditions (13.10) at time $t = 0$ we have

$E(0) = 0$. We shall show that $E(t)$ is a constant quantity on any solution of equation (13.9) subject to the boundary conditions (13.11). In fact, on differentiating (13.12) we obtain

$$\frac{dE(t)}{dt} = \int_0^l \left[ \rho(x) \frac{\partial \omega}{\partial t} \frac{\partial^2 \omega}{\partial t^2} + p(x) \frac{\partial \omega}{\partial x} \frac{\partial^2 \omega}{\partial x \partial t} + q(x)\omega \frac{\partial \omega}{\partial t} \right] dx.$$

and integrating the middle term by parts we obtain

$$\frac{dE(t)}{dt} = \int_0^l \left[ \rho(x) \frac{\partial^2 \omega}{\partial t^2} - \frac{\partial}{\partial x} \left( p(x) \frac{\partial \omega}{\partial x} \right) + q(x)\omega \right] \frac{\partial \omega}{\partial t} \, dx +$$

$$+ \, p(x) \frac{\partial \omega}{\partial x} \frac{\partial \omega}{\partial t} \Big|_{x=0}^{x=l}.$$

Hence, in view of equation (13.9) and the boundary conditions (13.11), it follows that $dE(t)/dt = 0$, so that $E(t) = $ const, but $E(0) = 0$ and therefore $E(t) \equiv 0$. From (13.12) we then have

$$\frac{\partial \omega}{\partial x} = \frac{\partial \omega}{\partial t} = 0,$$

i.e. $\omega(x, t) = $ const in $\bar{Q}$. Since in view of (13.10) $\omega(x, t) = 0$ when $t = 0$, it follows that $\omega(x, t) \equiv 0$ in $\bar{Q}$, which was to be proved.

*Remark.* The solution of the mixed problem is also unique when the boundary conditions given by (13.8) are replaced by the more complicated conditions

$$\frac{\partial u}{\partial x} - h_1 u \Big|_{x=0} = 0, \quad \frac{\partial u}{\partial x} + h_2 u \Big|_{x=l} = 0, \tag{13.13}$$

where $h_1 \geqslant 0$, $h_2 \geqslant 0$ are constants.

## 3. Continuous dependence of the solution of the mixed problem on the initial conditions.

*Theorem. Suppose we have two solutions $u_1(x, t)$ and $u_2(x, t)$ of equation (13.6) in the rectangle $Q$ which both satisfy the boundary* *conditions given by* (13.8) *and*

$$u_1|_{t=0} = \varphi_0^{(1)}(x), \quad \frac{\partial u_1}{\partial t}\bigg|_{t=0} = \varphi_1^{(1)}(x),$$

$$u_2|_{t=0} = \varphi_0^{(2)}(x), \quad \frac{\partial u_2}{\partial t}\bigg|_{t=0} = \varphi_1^{(2)}(x).$$

*If the differences*

$$\varphi_0^{(1)}(x) - \varphi_0^{(2)}(x) = \varphi_0(x), \quad \varphi_1^{(1)}(x) - \varphi_1^{(2)}(x) = \varphi_1(x)$$

*and the first derivative $\varphi_0'(x)$ are small enough throughout* [0, *l*] *in absolute magnitude, then the difference*

$$u_1(x, t) - u_2(x, t) = u(x, t)$$

*is as small in absolute magnitude as desired throughout Q.*

*Proof.* The function $u = u_1 - u_2$ satisfies the homogeneous equation

$$\rho(x) \frac{\partial^2 u}{\partial t^2} - \frac{\partial}{\partial x}\left(p(x) \frac{\partial u}{\partial x}\right) + q(x)u = 0, \tag{13.14}$$

subject to the homogeneous boundary conditions

$$u|_{x=0} = 0, \quad u|_{x=l} = 0 \tag{13.15}$$

and the initial data

$$u|_{t=0} = \varphi_0(x), \quad \frac{\partial u}{\partial t}\bigg|_{t=0} = \varphi_1(x). \tag{13.16}$$

Consider again the energy integral

$$E(t) = \tfrac{1}{2} \int_0^l \left[\rho(x)\left(\frac{\partial u}{\partial t}\right)^2 + p(x)\left(\frac{\partial u}{\partial x}\right)^2 + q(x)u^2\right]dx, \tag{13.17}$$

We have shown in § 13 that $E(t)$ remains constant on any solution of equation (13.14) which satisfies the boundary conditions (13.15). Therefore $E(t) = E(0)$ $(0 \leqslant t \leqslant T)$ or, in view of (13.16),

$$\int_0^l \left[\rho(x)\left(\frac{\partial u}{\partial t}\right)^2 + p(x)\left(\frac{\partial u}{\partial x}\right)^2 + q(x)u^2\right]dx =$$

$$= \int_0^l [\rho(x)\varphi_1^2(x) + p(x)\varphi_0'^2(x) + q(x)\varphi_0^2(x)]\,dx.$$

Suppose that $M = \max\limits_{[0, l]} \{\rho(x), p(x), q(x)\}$. In that case

$$\int_0^l \left[ \rho(x) \left(\frac{\partial u}{\partial t}\right)^2 + p(x) \left(\frac{\partial u}{\partial x}\right)^2 + q(x)u^2 \right] dx \leqslant$$

$$\leqslant M \int_0^l [\varphi_1^2(x) + \varphi_0'^2(x) + \varphi_0^2(x)] \, dx$$

or, since the right-hand side is small, we find that for any $t$ between 0 and $T$

$$\int_0^l \left[ \rho(x) \left(\frac{\partial u}{\partial t}\right)^2 + p(x) \left(\frac{\partial u}{\partial x}\right)^2 + q(x)u^2 \right] dx < \varepsilon^2$$

and therefore

$$\int_0^l p(x) \left(\frac{\partial u}{\partial x}\right)^2 dx < \varepsilon^2.$$

We have

$$u(x, t) - u(0, t) = \int_0^x \frac{\partial u}{\partial x} \, dx,$$

$$|u(x, t)| \leqslant \int_0^x \left| \frac{\partial u}{\partial x} \right| dx = \int_0^x \frac{1}{\sqrt{p(x)}} \, \sqrt{p(x)} \left| \frac{\partial u}{\partial x} \right| dx \leqslant$$

$$\leqslant \left[ \int_0^x \frac{dx}{p(x)} \int_0^x p(x) \left(\frac{\partial u}{\partial x}\right)^2 dx \right]^{\frac{1}{2}} \leqslant$$

$$\leqslant \left[ \int_0^l \frac{dx}{p(x)} \int_0^l p(x) \left(\frac{\partial u}{\partial x}\right)^2 dx \right]^{\frac{1}{2}} \leqslant K\varepsilon,$$

where $K$ is a constant. Therefore, $u(x, t)$ is small throughout the rectangle $Q$, which was to be proved.

*Remark.* The continuous dependence of the solution on the initial data can also be proved for the more general boundary conditions

$$\frac{\partial u}{\partial x} - h_1 u \bigg|_{x=0} = 0, \quad \frac{\partial u}{\partial x} + h_2 u \bigg|_{x=l} = 0,$$

where $h_1 \geqslant 0$, $h_2 \geqslant 0$ are constants.

### § 14. Fourier's method

### 1. Fourier's method for the equation of free oscillations of a string.

Fourier's method, or the method of separation of variables, is one of the most widely used methods for solving partial differential equations. We shall illustrate it by a number of examples, and will begin with the simple case of a string fixed at both ends. This problem can be reduced to the solution of the equation

$$\frac{\partial^2 u}{\partial t^2} = a^2 \frac{\partial^2 u}{\partial x^2} \tag{14.1}$$

subject to the boundary conditions

$$u|_{x=0} = 0, \quad u|_{x=l} = 0 \tag{14.2}$$

and the initial conditions

$$u|_{t=0} = \varphi_0(x), \quad \frac{\partial u}{\partial t}\bigg|_{t=0} = \varphi_1(x). \tag{14.3}$$

To begin with, we shall seek special solutions of (14.1), which are not identically equal to zero, in the form of the product

$$u(x, t) = X(x)\, T(t), \tag{14.4}$$

subject to the boundary conditions (14.2). Substituting (14.4) into (14.1) we obtain

$$T''(t)\, X(x) = a^2 T(t)\, X''(x)$$

or

$$\frac{T''(t)}{a^2 T(t)} = \frac{X''(x)}{X(x)}. \tag{14.5}$$

The left-hand side of the latter equation is a function of $t$ only, whilst the right hand side is a function of $x$ only. This is only possible if both are equal to the same constant. If we denote this constant by $-\lambda$, we obtain from (14.5) the following two ordinary differential equations:

$$T''(t) + a^2\lambda T(t) = 0, \tag{14.6}$$

$$X''(x) + \lambda X(x) = 0. \tag{14.7}$$

In order to obtain non-trivial solutions, i.e. solutions which do not vanish identically, in the form of (14.4) subject to the boundary conditions (14.2), we must find the non-trivial solutions of equation (14.7) which satisfy the boundary conditions

$$X(0) = 0, \quad X(l) = 0. \tag{14.8}$$

We thus arrive at the following problem: it is required to find those values of the parameter $\lambda$ for which equation (14.7) has non-trivial solutions satisfying the boundary conditions given by (14.8).

These values of $\lambda$ are called the *eigenvalues*, and the corresponding solutions are the *eigenfunctions* of the boundary value problem as specified by (14.7) and (14.8).

We shall now determine the eigenvalues and eigenfunctions of the problem defined by (14.7) and (14.8). We must distinguish three cases, i.e. $\lambda < 0$, $\lambda = 0$, and $\lambda > 0$.

(1) When $\lambda < 0$, the general solution of (14.7) is

$$X(x) = C_1 e^{\sqrt{-\lambda}x} + C_2 e^{-\sqrt{-\lambda}x},$$

where $C_1$ and $C_2$ are arbitrary constants. Substituting this into the boundary conditions given by (14.8) we obtain

$$C_1 + C_2 = 0, \quad C_1 e^{\sqrt{-\lambda}l} + C_2 e^{-\sqrt{-\lambda}l} = 0. \tag{14.9}$$

It is clear that the determinant of this set of equations is not equal to zero, and therefore $C_1 = 0$ and $C_2 = 0$. Consequently, $X(x) \equiv 0$.

(2) When $\lambda = 0$, the general solution of (14.7) is of the form

$$X(x) = C_1 + C_2 x.$$

The boundary conditions (14.8) now yield

$$C_1 + C_2 \cdot 0 = 0, \quad C_1 + C_2 l = 0.$$

and hence $C_1 = 0$, $C_2 = 0$ so that $X(x) \equiv 0$.

(3) When $\lambda > 0$ the general solution of (14.7) is

$$X(x) = C_1 \cos \sqrt{\lambda}x + C_2 \sin \sqrt{\lambda}x.$$

On substituting this into (14.8) we obtain

$$C_1 \cdot 1 + C_2 \cdot 0 = 0, \quad C_1 \cos \sqrt{\lambda}l + C_2 \sin \sqrt{\lambda}l = 0.$$

From the first equation it follows that $C_1 = 0$, whereas the second yields $C_2 \sin \sqrt{\lambda}l = 0$. We must assume that $C_2 \neq 0$, since otherwise $X(x) \equiv 0$. Therefore

$$\sin \sqrt{\lambda}l = 0, \quad \text{i.e. } \sqrt{\lambda} = \frac{k\pi}{l},$$

where $k$ is an integer. It follows that non-trivial solutions of the problem defined by (14.7) and (14.8) are possible only when

$$\lambda_k = \left(\frac{k\pi}{l}\right)^2 \qquad (k = 1, 2, 3, \ldots).$$

Apart from a constant factor, the corresponding eigenfunctions are

$$X_k(x) = \sin \frac{k\pi x}{l}.$$

We note that positive and negative values of $k$ which are equal in absolute magnitude yield equal values of $\lambda$ ($\lambda_{-k} = \lambda_k$), and that the corresponding eigenfunctions differ only by a constant factor. We can therefore confine $k$ to integral positive values.

When $\lambda = \lambda_k$, the general solution of (14.6) is

$$T_k(t) = a_k \cos \frac{k\pi at}{l} + b_k \sin \frac{k\pi at}{l},$$

where $a_k$ and $b_k$ are arbitrary constants.

It follows that the functions

$$u_k(x, t) = X_k(x) T_k(t) = \left(a_k \cos \frac{k\pi at}{l} + b_k \sin \frac{k\pi at}{l}\right) \sin \frac{k\pi x}{l}$$

satisfy equation (14.1) and the boundary conditions (14.2) for any

$a_k$ and $b_k$. Since equation (14.1) is linear and homogeneous, any finite sum of such solutions will also be a solution. This is also so for the series

$$u(x, t) = \sum_{k=1}^{\infty} \left( a_k \cos \frac{k\pi a t}{l} + b_k \sin \frac{k\pi a t}{l} \right) \sin \frac{k\pi x}{l}, \qquad (14.10)$$

if it converges uniformly and each of its terms can be differentiated twice with respect to $x$ and $t$. Since each of the terms in (14.10) satisfies the boundary conditions (14.2), these conditions are also satisfied by the whole series, i.e. by the function $u(x, t)$. All that remains is to determine the constants $a_k$ and $b_k$ so that the initial conditions given by (14.3) are also satisfied.

Differentiating (14.10) with respect to $t$ we obtain

$$\frac{\partial u}{\partial t} = \sum_{k=1}^{\infty} \frac{k\pi a}{l} \left( -a_k \sin \frac{k\pi a t}{l} + b_k \cos \frac{k\pi a t}{l} \right) \sin \frac{k\pi x}{l}. \qquad (14.11)$$

and if we set $t = 0$ in (14.10) and (14.11) we obtain from the initial conditions (14.3)

$$\varphi_0(x) = \sum_{k=1}^{\infty} a_k \sin \frac{k\pi x}{l}, \quad \varphi_1(x) \sum_{k=1}^{\infty} \frac{k\pi a}{l} b_k \sin \frac{k\pi x}{l}. \qquad (14.12)$$

These formulae are Fourier expansions of $\varphi_0(x)$ and $\varphi_1(x)$ in the interval $(0, l)$. The expansion coefficients are given by the well-known formulae

$$a_k = \frac{2}{l} \int_0^l \varphi_0(x) \sin \frac{k\pi x}{l}, \quad b_k = \frac{2}{k\pi a} \int_0^l \varphi_1(x) \sin \frac{k\pi x}{l} dx.$$

It follows that the solution of the problem defined by (14.1)–(14.3) is given by (14.10) with $a_k$ and $b_k$ given by (14.13).

*Theorem. If $\varphi_0(x)$ is twice continuously differentiable in the interval $(0, l)$, has a piecewise continuous third derivative and satisfies the conditions*

$$\varphi_0(0) = \varphi_0(l) = 0, \quad \varphi_0''(0) = \varphi_0''(l) = 0, \qquad (14.14)$$

*whilst $\varphi_1(x)$ is continuously differentiable, has a piecewise continuous* *second derivative and satisfies the conditions*

$$\varphi_1(0) = \varphi_1(l) = 0, \tag{14.15}$$

*then the function $u(x, t)$ is given by the series (14.10), has continuous second order derivatives and satisfies equation (14.1), boundary conditions (14.2) and initial conditions (14.3). Each term in (14.10) can then be differentiated twice with respect to x and t and the resulting series converge absolutely and uniformly for $0 \leqslant x \leqslant l$ and any t.*
*Proof.* Integrating (14.3) by parts and recalling (14.14) and (14.15), we obtain

$$a_k = -\left(\frac{l}{\pi}\right)^3 \frac{b_k^{(3)}}{k^3}, \quad b_k = -\left(\frac{l}{\pi}\right)^3 \frac{a_k^{(2)}}{k^3}, \tag{14.16}$$

where

$$b_k^{(3)} = \frac{2}{l} \int_0^l \varphi_0'''(x) \cos\frac{k\pi x}{l} \, dx, \quad a_k^{(2)} = \frac{2}{l} \int_0^l \frac{1}{a} \varphi_1''(x) \sin\frac{k\pi x}{l} \, dx. \tag{14.17}$$

It is easy to see that the series

$$\sum_{k=1}^{\infty} \frac{|a_k^{(2)}|}{k}, \quad \sum_{k=1}^{\infty} \frac{|b_k^{(3)}|}{k} \tag{14.18}$$

convergenec since

$$\frac{|a_k^{(2)}|}{k} \leqslant \frac{1}{2}\left[\frac{1}{k^2} + |a_k^{(2)}|^2\right], \quad \frac{|b_k^{(3)}|}{k} \leqslant \frac{1}{2}\left[\frac{1}{k^2} + |b_k^{(3)}|\right],$$

The series

$$\sum_{k=1}^{\infty} |a_k^{(2)}|^2, \quad \sum_{k=1}^{\infty} |b_k^{(3)}|^2$$

also converge.
Substituting (14.16) into (14.10) we obtain

$$u(x,t) = -\left(\frac{l}{\pi}\right)^3 \sum_{k=1}^{\infty} \frac{1}{k^3}\left(b_k^{(3)} \cos\frac{k\pi at}{l} + a_k^{(2)} \sin\frac{k\pi at}{l}\right) \sin\frac{k\pi x}{l}. \tag{14.19}$$

This must converge because

$$\left(\frac{l}{\pi}\right)^3 \sum_{k=1}^{\infty} \frac{1}{k^3} (|b_k^{(3)}| + |a_k^{(2)}|),$$

is known to converge. It follows that the series given by (14.10) converges absolutely and uniformly. In view of (14.18) it is easy to show that each term in (14.10) can be differentiated twice with respect to $x$ and $t$. This proves the theorem.

Let us return now to the solution of the problem defined by (14.1)–(14.3), which is given by (14.10). Substituting

$$a_k = A_k \sin \varphi_k, \quad b_k = A_k \cos \varphi_k,$$

this solution may be written in the form

$$u(x, t) = \sum_{k=1}^{\infty} A_k \sin \frac{k\pi x}{l} \sin \left(\frac{k\pi at}{l} + \varphi_k\right). \tag{14.20}$$

Each term in this series represents a so-called *standing wave* in which each point on the string executes a *harmonic oscillatory motion* with the same phase $\varphi_k$, amplitude $A_k \sin (k\pi x/l)$ and frequency $\omega_k = k\pi a/l$.

Sounds may be classified as musical and non-musical, the former being called *notes* and the latter *noise*. Notes can be conveniently arranged in sequences in accordance with their *pitch* which can be distinguished by most people. Notes which cannot be distinguished by the human ear are called *tones*.

An oscillating string produces sound whose pitch depends on the frequency of the oscillations. The frequency of the fundamental (lowest) tone is given by $\omega_1 = (\pi/l)\sqrt{T_0/\rho}$. Tones corresponding to higher frequencies are referred to as *overtones*. Overtones whose frequencies are multiples of the fundamental frequency are called *harmonics*. The fundamental tone will be referred to as the first harmonic, the tone with frequency $\omega_2 = 2\omega_1$ will be called the second harmonic, and so on.

The solution given by (14.20) is a combination of the various harmonics whose amplitudes, and therefore the effect on the ear in the case of an oscillating string, usually fall off rapidly with increasing $k$. They combine to produce the *timbre* which is different for different musical instruments, and is due to the presence of the various harmonics.

There are very few oscillatory systems with harmonic overtones, but the few that do exist are basic to the design of practically all musical instruments. This is due to the fact that sound with harmonic overtones is, musically, particularly acceptable.

The amplitude of the $n$-th harmonic vanishes at the points

$$x = 0, \frac{l}{n}, \frac{2l}{n}, \ldots, \frac{(n-1)l}{n}, l \tag{14.21}$$

since at these points $\sin(n\pi x/l) = 0$. The points defined by (14.21) are called the *nodes* of the $n$-th harmonic.

The amplitude of the $n$-th harmonic reaches its maximum value at the points

$$x = \frac{l}{2n}, \frac{3l}{2n}, \ldots, \frac{(2n-1)l}{2n} \tag{14.22}$$

since the function $\sin(n\pi x/l)$ assumes its maximum absolute value at these points. The points defined by (14.22) are called the *antinodes* of the $n$-th harmonic.

If we immobilise an oscillating string exactly at the midpoint, i.e. at the antinode of the fundamental, this will ensure that the amplitudes of all other tones having an antinode at this point will also vanish, i.e. all the odd harmonics will be suppressed, but even harmonics which have a node at the midpoint will be unaffected. We will thus be left with only the even harmonics and the lowest frequency will be $\omega_2 = (2\pi/l)\sqrt{T/\rho}$. The string will thus oscillate in a mode higher by an octave, i.e. the number of oscillations per second will be higher by a factor of 2.

**2. General Fourier method.** In this section we shall use Fourier's method to solve a mixed problem without rigorously justifying the final results.

Consider the hyperbolic equation

$$\rho(x) \frac{\partial^2 u}{\partial t^2} = \frac{\partial}{\partial x}\left(p(x) \frac{\partial u}{\partial x}\right) - q(x)u, \tag{14.23}$$

where $\rho(x)$, $p(x)$, $p'(x)$ and $q(x)$ are continuous in $0 \leqslant x \leqslant l$ and

$$p(x) \geqslant p_0 > 0, \quad \rho(x) \geqslant \rho_0 > 0, \quad q(x) \geqslant 0.$$

Suppose that it is required to find the solution of (14.23) which satisfies the homogeneous boundary conditions

$$\alpha u(0, t) + \beta \frac{\partial u(0, t)}{\partial x} = 0,$$

$$\gamma u(l, t) + \delta \frac{\partial u(l, t)}{\partial x} = 0,$$

(14.24)

where the constants $\alpha$, $\beta$, $\gamma$ and $\delta$ are such that $\alpha^2 + \beta^2 \neq 0$, $\gamma^2 + \delta^2 \neq 0$, and also the initial conditions

$$u|_{t=0} = \varphi_0(x), \quad \frac{\partial u}{\partial t}\bigg|_{t=0} = \varphi_1(x).$$

(14.25)

To begin with, we shall seek the non-trivial solutions of (14.23) in the form of the product

$$u(x, t) = X(x)\, T(t),$$

(14.26)

subject to the boundary conditions given by (14.24). Substituting (14.26) into (14.23) we obtain

$$T(t)\frac{d}{dx}[p(x)\, X'(x)] - q(x)\, X(x)\, T(t) = \rho(x)\, X(x)\, T''(t)$$

or

$$\frac{\dfrac{d}{dx}[p(x)\, X'(x)] - q(x)\, X(x)}{\rho(x)\, X(x)} = \frac{T''(t)}{T(t)}.$$

(14.27)

The left-hand side of the latter equation is a function of $x$ only, and the right-hand side a function of $t$ only. This is possible only if both are equal to the same constant. Let us denote this constant by $-\lambda$ so that (14.27) gives the following two ordinary differential equations

$$T''(t) + \lambda T(t) = 0,$$

(14.28)

$$\frac{d}{dx}[p(x)\, X'(x)] + [\lambda\rho(x) - q(x)]\, X(x) = 0.$$

(14.29)

In order to obtain non-trivial solutions of (14.23) in the form given by (14.26) subject to the boundary conditions (14.24), it is necessary that the function $X(x)$ should satisfy the boundary conditions

$$\alpha X(0) + \beta X'(0) = 0,$$
$$\gamma X(l) + \delta X'(l) = 0. \tag{14.30}$$

We thus arrive at the following eigenvalue problem: *It is required to find values of the parameter $\lambda$ for which there exist non-trivial solutions of* (14.29) *which satisfy the boundary conditions* (14.30).

Those values of $\lambda$ for which the problem defined by (14.29) and (14.30) has non-trivial solutions are called *eigenvalues,* and the solutions themselves are called *eigenfunctions.* Since equation (14.29) and the boundary conditions given by (14.30) are homogeneous, the eigenfunctions can be determined only to within a constant factor. It is easy to see that to each eigenvalue there corresponds only one linearly independent eigenfunction. In fact, let us suppose that to a given $\lambda$ there correspond two linearly independent solutions of (14.25) which satisfy the boundary conditions given by (14.30). We then find that the general solution of (14.29) also satisfies these conditions. This is, however, impossible, since we can always find a solution of (14.29) with initial values $X(0)$ and $X'(0)$ which will not satisfy the first of the boundary conditions in (14.30).

It may be shown that for our problem there exists an infinite set of real eigenvalues

$$\lambda_1 < \lambda_2 < \lambda_3 < \ldots < \lambda_n < \ldots, \qquad \lim_{n \to \infty} \lambda_n = +\infty.$$

To each eigenvalue $\lambda_k$ there corresponds an eigenfunction $X_k(x)$ which is determined to within a constant factor. Let us choose this factor so that

$$\int_0^l \rho(x) X_k^2(x) \, dx = 1. \tag{14.31}$$

Eigenfunctions which have this property are said to be *normalised.* We shall show that eigenfunctions corresponding to different eigenvalues are *orthogonal* with a weight $\rho(x)$ in the interval $(0, l)$, i.e.

$$\int_0^l \rho(x) X_k(x) X_m(x) dx = 0 \qquad (k \neq m). \tag{14.32}$$

In fact, suppose that $\lambda_k$ and $\lambda_m$ are two different eigenvalues, and that $X_k(x)$ and $X_m(x)$ are the corresponding eigenfunctions, so that

$$\frac{d}{dx} [p(x) X_k'(x)] + [\lambda_k \rho(x) - q(x)] X_k(x) = 0,$$

$$\frac{d}{dx} [p(x) X_m'(x)] + [\lambda_m \rho(x) - q(x)] X_m(x) = 0.$$

If we multiply the first equation by $X_m(x)$ and the second by $X_k(x)$, and subtract one from the other, we obtain

$$X_m(x) \frac{d}{dx} [p(x) X_k'(x)] - X_k(x) \frac{d}{dx} [p(x) X_m'(x)] +$$

$$+ (\lambda_k - \lambda_m) \rho(x) X_k(x) X_m(x) = 0,$$

which can be rewritten in the form

$$(\lambda_k - \lambda_m) \rho(x) X_k(x) X_m(x) +$$

$$+ \frac{d}{dx} \{p(x)[X_m(x) X_k'(x) - X_k(x) X_m'(x)]\}.$$

Integrating this equation with respect to $x$ between 0 and $l$, we obtain

$$(\lambda_m - \lambda_k) \int_0^l \rho(x) X_k X_m(x) dx =$$

$$= p(x)[X_m(x) X_k'(x) - X_k(x) X_m'(x)]|_{x=0}^{x=l}.$$

In view of the boundary conditions (14.30), it is evident that the right-hand side must vanish, i.e.

$$(\lambda_m - \lambda_k) \int_0^l \rho(x) X_k(x) X_m(x) dx = 0.$$

Since $\lambda_m \neq \lambda_k$, we finally have

$$\int_0^l \rho(x) X_k(x) X_m(x) dx = 0,$$

which was to be established.

The orthogonal property of eigenfunctions ensures that all the eigenvalues are real.

Suppose now that $\lambda_k$ are the eigenvalues and $X_k(x)$ are the eigenfunctions forming an orthogonal and normalised system. We have

$$\frac{d}{dx}[p(x)X_k'(x)] - q(x)X_k(x) = -\lambda_k\rho(x)X_k(x).$$

Multiplying both parts by $X_k(x)$, integrating and recalling equation (14.31), we obtain

$$\lambda_k = -\int_0^l \left\{\frac{d}{dx}[p(x)X_k'(x)] - q(x)X_k(x)X_k(x)\,dx,\right.$$

and hence, on integrating the first term by parts, we have

$$\lambda_k = \int_0^l [p(x)X_k'^2(x) + q(x)X_k^2(x)]\,dx -$$

$$- [p(x)X_k(x)X_k'(x)]\big|_{x=0}^{x=l}. \tag{14.33}$$

If we suppose that the second term on the right is not positive, i.e.

$$[p(x)X_k(x)X_k'(x)]_{x=0}^{x=l} \leqslant 0. \tag{14.34}$$

then, since $p(x) \geqslant p_0 > 0$, $q(x) \geqslant 0$, it follows from (14.33) that all the eigenvalues of the problem defined by (14.29) and (14.30) are non-negative.

We note that the condition given by (14.34) is satisfied in the most frequently encountered boundary conditions:

1) $X(0) = 0$, $X(l) = 0$;  2) $X'(0) = 0$, $X'(l) = 0$;

3) $X'(0) - h_1 X(0) = 0$, $X'(l) + h_2 X(l) = 0$,

where $k_1$ and $k_2$ are positive numbers.

Having established some of the properties of eigenvalues and eigenfunctions, let us return now to equation (14.28). Its general solution for $\lambda = \lambda_k$ is of the form

$$T_k(t) = A_k \cos\sqrt{\lambda_k}\,t + B_k \sin\sqrt{\lambda_k}\,t,$$

where $A_k$ and $B_k$ are arbitrary constants. Therefore, according to (14.26), any function

$$u_k(x, t) = X_k(x) T_k(t) = (A_k \cos \sqrt{\lambda_k}\, t + B_k \sin \sqrt{\lambda_k}\, t) X_k(x)$$

will be a solution of (14.23) satisfying the boundary conditions (14.24).

In order to satisfy the initial conditions given by (14.25), consider the series

$$u(x, t) = \sum_{k=1}^{\infty} (A_k \cos \sqrt{\lambda_k}\, t + B_k \sin \sqrt{\lambda_k}\, t) X_k(x). \tag{14.35}$$

If this series, and the series obtained from it by differentiating twice term by term with respect to $x$ and $t$, converge uniformly, then it is a solution of (14.23) subject to the boundary conditions given by (14.24).

To satisfy the initial conditions given (14.25), it is necessary that

$$u|_{t=0} = \varphi_0(x) = \sum_{k=1}^{\infty} A_k X_k(x), \tag{14.36}$$

$$\frac{\partial u}{\partial t}\bigg|_{t=0} = \varphi_1(x) = \sum_{k=1}^{\infty} B_k \sqrt{\lambda_k}\, X_k(x). \tag{14.37}$$

We have therefore arrived at a problem involving the expansion of an arbitrary function in terms of the eigenfunctions $X_k(x)$ of the boundary-value problem (14.29)–(14.30). If we suppose that the series given by (14.36) and (14.37) converge uniformly, we can determine the coefficients $A_k$ and $B_k$ by multiplying both sides of these equations by $\rho(x) X_k(x)$ and integrate with respect to $x$ between 0 and $l$. In this way, bearing in mind (14.31) and (14.32), we obtain

$$A_k = \int_0^l \rho(x)\, \varphi_0(x)\, X_k(x)\, dx, \quad B_k = \frac{1}{\sqrt{\lambda_k}} \int_0^l \rho(x)\, \varphi_1(x)\, X_k(x)\, dx.$$

Substituting this into (14.35), we will obtain the solution of the mixed problem (14.23)–(14.25), provided the series given by (14.25) and the series obtained from it by differentiating term by term twice with respect to $x$ and $t$ are uniformly convergent.

**3. Forced oscillations of a string fixed at the ends.** Consider the forced oscillations of a uniform string fixed at the ends under the action of an external force $F(x, t)$ per unit length. This problem may be reduced to the solution of the equation

$$\frac{\partial^2 u}{\partial t^2} = a^2 \frac{\partial^2 u}{\partial x^2} + f(x, t) \quad \left( f(x, t) = \frac{F(x, t)}{\rho} \right) \tag{14.38}$$

subject to the boundary conditions

$$u|_{x=0} = 0, \quad u|_{x=l} = 0 \tag{14.39}$$

and initial conditions

$$u|_{t=0} = \varphi_0(x), \quad \frac{\partial u}{\partial t}\bigg|_{t=0} = \varphi_1(x). \tag{14.40}$$

We shall seek the solution of this problem in the form

$$u = v + w, \tag{14.41}$$

where $v$ is the solution of the inhomogeneous equation

$$\frac{\partial^2 v}{\partial t^2} = a^2 \frac{\partial^2 v}{\partial x^2} + f(x, t), \tag{14.42}$$

satisfying the boundary conditions

$$v|_{x=0} = 0, \quad v|_{x=l} = 0 \tag{14.43}$$

and initial conditions

$$v|_{t=0} = 0, \quad \frac{\partial v}{\partial t}\bigg|_{t=0} = 0, \tag{14.44}$$

whilst $w$ is a solution of the inhomogeneous equation

$$\frac{\partial^2 w}{\partial t^2} = a^2 \frac{\partial^2 w}{\partial x^2}, \tag{14.45}$$

satisfying the boundary conditions

$$w|_{x=0} = 0, \quad w|_{x=l} = 0 \tag{14.46}$$

and initial conditions

$$w|_{t=0} = \varphi_0(x), \quad \frac{\partial w}{\partial t}\bigg|_{t=0} = \varphi_1(x). \tag{14.47}$$

The function $v$ represents the *forced* oscillations of a string, i.e. oscillations which are under the action of an external disturbing force, but with no initial disturbance. The function $w$ represents the *free* oscillations of the string, i.e. oscillations which take place in the absence of external forces and are a consequence of an initial disturbance. Since the problem of free oscillations was considered in § 1, we shall now confine our attention to the forced oscillations only. As in the case of free oscillations, we shall seek $v$ in the form

$$v(x, t) = \sum_{k=1}^{\infty} T_k(t) \sin \frac{k\pi x}{l}, \tag{14.48}$$

so that the boundary conditions (14.43) are automatically satisfied, assuming, of course, that (14.48) converges uniformly.
We shall now define $T_k(t)$ so that (14.48) satisfies (14.42) and the initial conditions (14.44).
Substituting (14.48) into (14.42), we obtain

$$\sum_{k=1}^{\infty} [T_k''(t) + \omega_k^2 T_k(t)] \sin \frac{k\pi x}{l} = f(x, t), \tag{14.49}$$

where

$$\omega_k = \frac{k\pi a}{l}. \tag{14.50}$$

Let us expand $f(x, t)$ in the interval $(0, l)$ into the Fourier series

$$f(x, t) = \sum_{k=1}^{\infty} f_k(t) \sin \frac{k\pi x}{l}, \tag{14.51}$$

where

$$f_k(t) = \frac{2}{l} \int_0^l f(x, t) \sin \frac{k\pi x}{l} \, dx. \tag{14.52}$$

Comparison of (14.49) and (14.51) for the same function $f(x, t)$ yields the differential equations

$$T_k''(t) + \omega_k^2 T_k(t) = f_k(t) \qquad (k = 1, 2, 3, \ldots), \tag{14.53}$$

which determine the function $T_k(t)$.

In order to ensure that the function $v$ given by (14.48) satisfies the initial conditions (14.44), it is sufficient to impose the following conditions on $T_k(t)$:

$$T_k(0) = 0, \quad T'_k(0) = 0 \qquad (k = 1, 2, 3, \ldots). \tag{14.54}$$

The solution of (14.53) subject to the initial conditions (14.54) is

$$T_k(t) = \frac{1}{\omega_k} \int_0^t f_k(\tau) \sin \omega_k(t - \tau) d\tau$$

or, substituting (14.52) for $f_k(\tau)$, we obtain

$$T_k(t) = \frac{2}{l\omega_k} \int_0^t \sin \omega_k(t - \tau) d\tau \int_0^l f(x, \tau) \sin \frac{k\pi x}{l} dx. \tag{14.55}$$

Substituting this expression for $T_k(t)$ into (14.48), we obtain the solution of the problem defined by (14.42)–(14.44), provided the series given by (14.48) and also the series obtained from it by differentiating term by term twice with respect to $x$ and $t$, converge uniformly. It may be shown that the uniform convergence of the series is ensured if the continuous function $f(x, t)$ has continuous partial derivatives with respect to $x$ up to the second order, and the conditions

$$f(0, t) = 0, \quad f(l, t) = 0.$$

are satisfied for all $t$.

It follows from the above discussion that the solution of (14.38)–(14.40) can be written in the form

$$u(x, t) = \sum_{k=1}^{\infty} T_k(t) \sin \frac{k\pi x}{l} +$$

$$+ \sum_{k=1}^{\infty} \left( a_k \cos \frac{k\pi a t}{l} + b_k \sin \frac{k\pi a t}{l} \right) \sin \frac{k\pi x}{l},$$

where $T_k(t)$ are given by (14.55) and

$$a_k = \frac{2}{l} \int_0^l \varphi_0(x) \sin \frac{k\pi x}{l} dx, \quad b_k = \frac{2}{k\pi a} \int_0^l \varphi_1(x) \sin \frac{k\pi x}{l} dx.$$

**4. Forced oscillations of a string with free ends.** Consider the forced oscillations of a uniform string under the action of an external force $F(x, t)$ whose ends are not fixed but move in a prescribed way. This problem may be reduced to the solution of the equation

$$\frac{\partial^2 u}{\partial t^2} = a^2 \frac{\partial^2 u}{\partial x^2} + f(x, t) \tag{14.56}$$

subject to the boundary conditions

$$u|_{x=0} = \kappa_1(t), \quad u|_{x=l} = \kappa_2(t) \tag{14.57}$$

and initial conditions

$$u|_{t=0} = \varphi_0(x), \quad \frac{\partial u}{\partial t}\bigg|_{t=0} = \varphi_1(x). \tag{14.58}$$

The problem defined by (14.56)–(14.58) can easily be reduced to a problem with homogeneous boundary conditions. In fact, consider the function

$$w(x, t) = \kappa_1(t) + [\kappa_2(t) - \kappa_1(t)] \frac{x}{l}. \tag{14.59}$$

It is clear that

$$w|_{x=0} = \kappa_1(t), \quad w|_{x=l} = \kappa_2(t). \tag{14.60}$$

We shall seek the solution of the problem (14.56)–(14.58) in the form

$$u = v + w, \tag{14.61}$$

where $w$ is a new unknown function.

In view of the boundary conditions given by (14.57) and (14.60), and the initial conditions (14.58), the function $v(x, t)$ must satisfy the boundary conditions

$$v|_{x=0} = 0, \quad v|_{x=l} = 0$$

and initial conditions

$$v|_{t=0} = u|_{t=0} - w|_{t=0} =$$
$$= \varphi_0(x) - \kappa_1(0) - [\kappa_2(0) - \kappa_1(0)] \frac{x}{l} = \bar{\varphi}_0(x),$$

$$\frac{\partial v}{\partial t}\Big|_{t=0} = \frac{\partial u}{\partial t}\Big|_{t=0} - \frac{\partial w}{\partial t}\Big|_{t=0} =$$

$$= \varphi_1(x) - \kappa_1'(0) - [\kappa_2'(0) - \kappa_1'(0)]\frac{x}{l} = \bar{\varphi}_1(x).$$

Substituting (14.61) into (14.56), we obtain

$$\frac{\partial^2 v}{\partial t^2} = a^2 \frac{\partial^2 v}{\partial x^2} + a^2 \frac{\partial^2 w}{\partial x^2} - \frac{\partial^2 w}{\partial t^2} + f(x, t)$$

or, in view of (14.59),

$$\frac{\partial^2 v}{\partial t^2} = a^2 \frac{\partial^2 v}{\partial x^2} + \bar{f}(x, t),$$

where

$$\bar{f}(x, t) = f(x, t) - \kappa_1''(t) - [\kappa_2''(t) - \kappa_1''(t)]\frac{x}{l}.$$

We have thus arrived at the following problem for the function $v(x, t)$:

$$\frac{\partial^2 v}{\partial t^2} = a^2 \frac{\partial^2 v}{\partial x^2} + \bar{f}(x, t),$$

$$v|_{x=0} = 0, \quad v|_{x=l} = 0,$$

$$v|_{t=0} = \bar{\varphi}_0(x), \quad \frac{\partial v}{\partial t}\Big|_{t=0} = \bar{\varphi}_1(x).$$

The solution of this problem was discussed in § 3.

**5. Fourier method in the multi-dimensional case.** Consider the equation

$$\frac{\partial^2 u}{\partial t^2} = L(u), \tag{14.62}$$

where

$$L(u) = \sum_{i,j=1}^{n} \frac{\partial}{\partial x_i}\left(a_{ij}(X)\frac{\partial u}{\partial x_j}\right) - a(X)u,$$

whose coefficients are defined in a finite connected domain $\Omega$ of

$X = (x_1, \ldots, x_n)$ and satisfies in $\varGamma$ the conditions

$$a(X) \geqslant 0, \quad a_{ij} = a_{ji}, \quad \sum_{i,j=1}^{n} a_{ij}\xi_i\xi_j \geqslant \alpha \sum_{i=1}^{n} \xi_i^2, \quad \alpha > 0. \qquad (14.63)$$

The second inequality expresses the fact that equation (14.62) is of the hyperbolic type.

Consider the following mixed problem for equation (14.62): it is required to determine in the cylinder $Q_T = \varOmega \times (0 < t < T)$, the solution of (14.62) which satisfies the initial conditions

$$u|_{t=0} = \varphi_0(X), \quad \frac{\partial u}{\partial t}\bigg|_{t=0} = \varphi_1(X) \qquad (14.64)$$

and the boundary condition

$$u|_S = 0 \text{ when } t \in [0, T], \qquad (14.65)$$

where $S$ is the boundary of $\varOmega$.

To begin with, we shall seek non-trivial solutions of (14.62) in the form of the product

$$u = v(X) T(t), \qquad (14.66)$$

subject to the boundary condition (14.65). Substituting (14.66) into (14.62), we obtain

$$v(X) T''(t) = \left[ \sum_{i,j=1}^{n} \frac{\partial}{\partial x_i} \left( a_{ij}(X) \frac{\partial v}{\partial x_j} \right) - a(X)v \right] T(t)$$

or

$$\frac{T''(t)}{T(t)} = \frac{L(v)}{v} = -\lambda,$$

whence

$$T''(t) + \lambda T(t) = 0, \qquad (14.67)$$

$$L(v) + \lambda v = 0. \qquad (14.68)$$

In order to obtain non-trivial solutions of (14.62) in the form of (14.66) subject to the boundary condition (14.65), it is necessary that $v(X)$ should satisfy the boundary condition

$$v|_S = 0. \qquad (14.69)$$

We thus arrive at the following eigenvalue problem: it is required to find those values of $\lambda$ for which equation (14.68) has non-trivial solutions satisfying the boundary condition (14.69).

These values of $\lambda$ are called the eigenvalues, and the corresponding solutions the eigenfunctions of the boundary value problem (14.68)–(14.69). It may be shown that the problem defined by (14.68)–(14.69) has an infinite set of eigenvalues

$$\lambda_1 \leqslant \lambda_2 \leqslant \ldots \leqslant \lambda_n \leqslant \ldots, \quad \lim_{n \to \infty} \lambda_n = \infty.$$

Since equation (14.68) and the boundary conditions (14.69) are inhomogeneous, the eigenfunctions $v_k(X)$ are determined to within an arbitrary constant. We can choose this factor so that

$$\int_{\Omega} v_k^2(X)\, dX = 1, \tag{14.70}$$

i.e. we can consider normalised eigenfunctions. Eigenfunctions corresponding to different eigenvalues are orthogonal, i.e.

$$\int_{\Omega} v_k(X)\, v_m(X)\, dX = 0, \qquad k \neq m. \tag{14.71}$$

This can be proved by an extension of the argument employed in the one-dimensional case. If to a given eigenvalue $\lambda_k$ there corresponds a number of linearly independent eigenfunctions, these functions can be made orthogonal, and consequently they may be regarded as orthogonal in pairs.

We may therefore consider that all the eigenfunctions of the problem defined by (14.68)–(14.69) form an orthogonal normalised system.

Let $\lambda_k$ be the eigenvalues and $v_k(X)$ the eigenfunctions forming an orthogonal normalised system. We have

$$L(v_k) = -\lambda_k v_k(X).$$

Multiplying both sides by $v_k(X)$ and integrating over $\Omega$ we obtain, in view of (14.70)

$$\lambda_k = -\int_{\Omega} v_k(X)\, L(v_k)\, dX =$$

$$= -\int_{\Omega} v_k(X) \left[ \sum_{i,j=1}^{n} \frac{\partial}{\partial x_i} \left( a_{ij}(X)\, \frac{\partial v_k}{\partial x_j} \right) - a(X)\, v_k(X) \right] dX$$

or, integrating the first sum by parts, we have

$$\lambda_k = \int_\Omega \left[ \sum_{i,j=1}^n a_{ij}(X) \, \frac{\partial v_k}{\partial x_i} \, \frac{\partial v_k}{\partial x_j} + a(X) \, v_k^2(X) \right] dX.$$

The integral over the boundary $S$ of $\Omega$ must vanish, since $v_k(X)|_S = 0$. In view of (14.63)

$$\lambda_k \geqslant \int_\Omega \left[ \alpha \sum_{i=1}^n \left( \frac{\partial v_k}{\partial x_i} \right)^2 + a(X) \, v_k^2(X) \right] dX,$$

and it follows that all the eigenvalues of (14.68)–(14.69) are positive. When $\lambda = \lambda_k$ equation (14.67) has solutions of the form

$$T_k(t) = A_k \cos \sqrt{\lambda_k}\, t + B_k \sin \sqrt{\lambda_k}\, t,$$

where $A_k$ and $B_k$ are arbitrary constants.
Therefore, according to (14.66) each function

$$u_k(X, t) = v_k(X) \, T_k(t) = (A_k \cos \sqrt{\lambda_k}\, t + B_k \sin \sqrt{\lambda_k}\, t)\, v_k(X)$$

is a solution of (14.62) subject to the boundary condition (14.65). Consider the series

$$u(X, t) = \sum_{k=1}^\infty (A_k \cos \sqrt{\lambda_k}\, t + B_k \sin \sqrt{\lambda_k}\, t)\, v_k(X). \qquad (14.72)$$

Substituting this into the initial conditions (14.64) we obtain

$$\varphi_0(X) = \sum_{k=1}^\infty A_k v_k(X), \quad \varphi_1(X) = \sum_{k=1}^\infty B_k \sqrt{\lambda_k}\, v_k(X).$$

from which we can easily show that

$$A_k = \int_\Omega \varphi_0(X) \, v_k(X) \, dX, \quad B_k = \frac{1}{\sqrt{\lambda_k}} \int_\Omega \varphi_1(X) \, v_k(X) \, dX.$$

Substituting this into (14.72), we obtain the solution of the problem defined by (14.62), (14.64) and (14.65), provided the series given by (14.72) and also the series obtained from it after differentiating term by term with respect to $x_i$ and $t$ twice, are uniformly convergent.

**6. Free oscillations of a rectangular membrane.** Consider the small oscillations of a uniform rectangular membrane with sides $p$, $q$, fixed along its edges. This problem can be reduced to the solution of the wave equation

$$\frac{\partial^2 u}{\partial t^2} = a^2 \left( \frac{\partial^2 u}{\partial x^2} + \frac{\partial^2 u}{\partial y^2} \right)$$
(14.73)

subject to the boundary conditions

$$u|_{x=0} = 0, \quad u|_{x=p} = 0, \quad u|_{y=0} = 0, \quad u|_{y=q} = 0$$
(14.74)

and initial conditions

$$u|_{t=0} = \varphi_0(x, y), \quad \frac{\partial u}{\partial t}\bigg|_{t=0} = \varphi_1(x, y).$$
(14.75)

We shall seek the initial conditions of (14.73) in the form

$$u(x, y, t) = T(t)\, v(x, y),$$
(14.76)

subject to the boundary conditions (14.74). Substituting (14.76) into equation (14.73), we obtain

$$\frac{T''(t)}{a^2 T(t)} = \frac{v_{xx} + v_{yy}}{v} = -k^2.$$

Hence, in view of the boundary conditions given by (14.74), we have

$$T''(t) + a^2 k^2 T(t) = 0,$$
(14.77)

and

$$\frac{\partial^2 v}{\partial x^2} + \frac{\partial^2 v}{\partial y^2} + k^2 v = 0,$$
(14.78)

$$v|_{x=0} = 0, \quad v|_{x=p} = 0, \quad v|_{y=0} = 0, \quad v|_{y=q} = 0.$$
(14.79)

We shall now find the eigenvalues and eigenfunctions of the problem defined by (14.78)–(14.79). Let

$$v(x, y) = X(x)\, Y(y).$$
(14.80)

Substituting this into (14.78), we obtain

$$\frac{Y''}{Y} + k^2 = -\frac{X''}{X},$$

which yields the following two equations

$$X''(x) + k_1^2 X(x) = 0, \quad Y''(y) + k_2^2 Y(y) = 0, \tag{14.81}$$

where

$$-k_2^2 + k^2 = k_1^2 \quad \text{or} \quad k^2 = k_1^2 + k_2^2. \tag{14.82}$$

The general solution of (14.81) is known to be

$$\begin{aligned} X(x) &= C_1 \cos k_1 x + C_2 \sin k_1 x, \\ Y(y) &= C_3 \cos k_2 y + C_4 \sin k_2 y. \end{aligned} \tag{14.83}$$

Substituting this into (14.79), we obtain

$$\begin{aligned} X(0) &= 0, \quad X(p) = 0, \\ Y(0) &= 0, \quad Y(q) = 0, \end{aligned} \tag{14.84}$$

from which it is clear that $C_1 = C_3 = 0$, and if we set $C_2 = C_4 = 1$, it turns out that

$$X(x) = \sin k_1 x, \quad Y(y) = \sin k_2 y, \tag{14.85}$$

where

$$\sin k_1 p = 0, \quad \sin k_2 q = 0. \tag{14.86}$$

It follows from (14.86) that $k_1$ and $k_2$ have an infinite set of values given by

$$k_{1,m} = \frac{m\pi}{p}, \quad k_{2,n} = \frac{n\pi}{q} \quad (m, n = 1, 2, 3, \ldots).$$

It then follows from (14.82) that the values of $k^2$ are

$$k_{m,n}^2 = k_{1,m}^2 + k_{2,n}^2 = \pi^2 \left( \frac{m^2}{p^2} + \frac{n^2}{q^2} \right). \tag{14.87}$$

Thus, in view of (14.80) and (14.85), the eigenfunctions

$$v_{mn}(x, y) = \sin \frac{m\pi x}{p} \sin \frac{n\pi y}{q} \tag{14.88}$$

of the boundary value problem (14.78)–(14.79) correspond to the eigenvalues given by (14.87).

Returning now to equation (14.77), we see that for each eigenvalue $k^2 = k^2_{mn}$, its general solution is of the form

$$T_{mn}(t) = A_{mn} \cos ak_{mn}t + B_{mn} \sin ak_{mn}t, \qquad (14.89)$$

where $A_{mn}$ and $B_{mn}$ are arbitrary constants.

We thus find that in view of (14.76), (14.88) and (14.89), the special solutions of (14.73) which satisfy the boundary conditions (14.74) are

$$u_{mn}(x, y, t) = (A_{mn} \cos ak_{mn}t + B_{mn} \sin ak_{mn}t) \sin \frac{m\pi x}{p} \sin \frac{n\pi y}{q}$$

$$(m, n = 1, 2, 3, \ldots).$$

In order to satisfy the initial conditions given by (14.75), let us construct the series

$$u(x, y, t) =$$

$$= \sum_{m,n=1}^{\infty} (A_{mn} \cos ak_{mn}t + B_{mn} \sin ak_{mn}t) \sin \frac{m\pi x}{p} \sin \frac{\pi n y}{q}.$$

$$(14.90)$$

If this series converges uniformly, and also the series obtained from it by differentiating term by term with respect to $x$, $y$ and $t$ twice, it will clearly satisfy (14.73) and the boundary conditions (14.74). To satisfy the initial conditions (14.75), it is necessary that

$$u|_{t=0} = \varphi_0(x, y) = \sum_{m,n=1}^{\infty} A_{mn} \sin \frac{m\pi x}{p} \sin \frac{n\pi y}{q},$$

$$\frac{\partial u}{\partial t}\bigg|_{t=0} = \varphi_1(x, y) = \sum_{m,n=1}^{\infty} ak_{mn}B_{mn} \sin \frac{m\pi x}{p} \sin \frac{\pi n y}{q}.$$

$$(14.91)$$

These formulae are the expansions of the functions $\varphi_0(x, y)$ and $\varphi_1(x, y)$ into double Fourier series. The expansion coefficients are given by

$$A_{mn} = \frac{4}{pq} \int_0^p \int_0^q \varphi_0(x, y) \sin \frac{m\pi x}{p} \sin \frac{n\pi y}{q} \, dx \, dy,$$

$$(14.92)$$

$$B_{mn} = \frac{4}{ak_{mn}pq} \int_0^p \int_0^q \varphi_1(x, y) \sin \frac{m\pi x}{p} \sin \frac{n\pi y}{q} \, dx \, dy.$$

Substitution of this into (14.90) leads to the solution of our problem. Let

$$A_{mn} = M_{mn} \sin \varphi_{mn}, \quad B_{mn} = M_{mn} \cos \varphi_{mn}.$$

The solution of (14.90) can then be written in the form

$$u(x, y, t) = \sum_{m,n=1}^{\infty} M_{mn} \sin \frac{m\pi x}{p} \sin \frac{n\pi y}{q} \sin (ak_{mn}t + \varphi_{mn}).$$

$$(14.93)$$

Each term in this series represents a standing wave in which each point of the membrane executes harmonic oscillatory motion with frequency $\omega_{mn} = a\pi\sqrt{m^2/p^2 + n^2/q^2}$. The oscillations of a membrane differ from the oscillations of a string in that for the latter, to each frequency of oscillations, there corresponds a particular form of the string which is simply divided by nodes into a number of equal parts. In the case of a membrane, it may turn out that to a given frequency there correspond a number of figures with different nodal lines, i.e. lines along which the amplitude of the oscillations is zero. This is most easily illustrated by the example of a square membrane for which $p = q = \pi$. In this case the frequency $\omega_{mn}$ is given by

$$\omega_{mn} = a\sqrt{m^2 + n^2},$$

from which it is evident that the fundamental is given by

$$u_{11} = M_{11} \sin x \sin y \sin (\omega_{11}t + \varphi_{11}),$$

and the corresponding frequency is $\omega_1 = a\sqrt{2}$. For this frequency the nodal lines lie along the edges of the square forming the membrane.

When $m = 1$, $n = 2$, or $m = 2$, $n = 1$, there are two overtones, namely

$$u_{12} = M_{12} \sin x \sin 2y \sin (\omega_{12}t + \varphi_{12}),$$
$$u_{21} = M_{21} \sin 2x \sin y \sin (\omega_{21}t + \varphi_{21})$$

with the same frequency $\omega_{12} = \omega_{21} = a\sqrt{5}$. It is clear that for this frequency (when $\varphi_{12} = \varphi_{21}$) the nodal lines are determined by

$$\alpha \sin x \sin 2y + \beta \sin 2x \sin y = 0$$

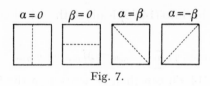

Fig. 7.

or

$$\alpha \cos y + \beta \cos x = 0.$$

The simplest of these are shown by the broken lines in fig. 7. More complicated nodal lines corresponding to the same frequency are obtained when $\alpha \neq \pm \beta$ and $\alpha, \beta \neq 0$.

**7. Free oscillations of a circular membrane.** Consider now the free oscillations of a circular membrane of radius $R$ with centre at the origin and fixed along its periphery. The problem may be reduced to the solution of the wave equation

$$\frac{\partial^2 u}{\partial x^2} + \frac{\partial^2 u}{\partial y^2} = \frac{1}{a^2} \frac{\partial^2 u}{\partial t^2}. \tag{14.94}$$

On introducing the polar coordinates

$$x = r \cos \theta, \quad y = r \sin \theta,$$

equation (14.94) can be transformed to read

$$\frac{\partial^2 u}{\partial r^2} + \frac{1}{r} \frac{\partial u}{\partial r} + \frac{1}{r^2} \frac{\partial^2 u}{\partial \theta^2} = \frac{1}{a^2} \frac{\partial^2 u}{\partial t^2} \tag{14.95}$$

with boundary condition

$$u|_{r=R} = 0 \tag{14.96}$$

and initial condition

$$u|_{t=0} = \varphi_0(r, \theta), \quad \frac{\partial u}{\partial t}\bigg|_{t=0} = \varphi_1(r, \theta). \tag{14.97}$$

Consider the case when the circular membrane executes radial oscillations, i.e. oscillations in which the displacement $u$ is a function of $r$ and $t$ only. These oscillations occur when the initial conditions are

$$u|_{t=0} = \varphi_0(r), \quad \frac{\partial u}{\partial t}\bigg|_{t=0} = \varphi_1(r), \tag{14.98}$$

where $\varphi_0(r)$ and $\varphi_1(r)$ are eigenfunctions in the interval $(0, R)$. Since in the case under consideration $u$ is independent of the angle $\theta$, equation (14.95) assumes the simpler form

$$\frac{\partial^2 u}{\partial r^2} + \frac{1}{r}\frac{\partial u}{\partial r} = \frac{1}{a^2}\frac{\partial^2 u}{\partial t^2}. \tag{14.99}$$

We shall seek the solutions of (14.99) in the form

$$u(r, t) = T(t)\,W(r), \tag{14.100}$$

subject to the boundary condition (14.96). Substituting (14.100) into (14.99), and separating the variables, we obtain

$$\frac{W''(r) + \dfrac{1}{r}\,W'(r)}{W(r)} = \frac{T''(t)}{a^2 T(t)} = -k^2,$$

which yields the two equations

$$T''(t) + k^2 a^2 T(t) = 0, \tag{14.101}$$

$$W''(r) + \frac{1}{r}\,W'(r) + k^2 W(r) = 0. \tag{14.102}$$

The latter equation is the Bessel equation whose solution is

$$W(r) = C_1 J_0(kr) + C_2 Y_0(kr),$$

where $C_1$ and $C_2$ are arbitrary constants and $J_0(kr)$ and $Y_0(kr)$ are zero order Bessel functions of the first and second kind [5]. Of these functions, only $J_0(kr)$ remains finite at $r = 0$, whilst $Y_0(kr)$ becomes infinite. We must therefore set $C_2 = 0$, since otherwise the displacement $u(r, t)$ becomes infinite at $r = 0$, which is physically impossible. The boundary condition (14.96) then requires that $C_1 J_0(kR) = 0$, or $J_0(kR) = 0$, since $C_1 \neq 0$. Substituting

$$kR = \mu, \tag{14.103}$$

we obtain

$$J_0(\mu) = 0. \tag{14.104}$$

which has an infinite number of real positive roots which we shall denote by $\mu_1, \mu_2, \mu_3, \ldots$ Using (14.103), we thus find that

$$k_n = \frac{\mu_n}{R} \qquad (n = 1, 2, 3, \ldots).$$

and when $k = k_m$, equation (14.101) has the solution

$$T_n(t) = a_n \cos \frac{a\mu_n t}{R} + b_n \sin \frac{a\mu_n t}{R},$$

where $a_n$ and $b_n$ are arbitrary constants.
In view of (14.100), the functions

$$u_n(r, t) = \left( a_n \cos \frac{a\mu_n t}{R} + b_n \sin \frac{a\mu_n t}{R} \right) J_0\left( \frac{\mu_n r}{R} \right)$$

satisfy equation (14.99) and boundary condition (14.96). Consider the series

$$u(r, t) = \sum_{n=1}^{\infty} \left( a_n \cos \frac{a\mu_n t}{R} + b_n \sin \frac{a\mu_n t}{R} \right) J_0\left( \frac{\mu_n r}{R} \right). \qquad (14.105)$$

Since we must satisfy the initial conditions (14.98), we have

$$\varphi_0(r) = \sum_{n=1}^{\infty} a_n J_0\left( \frac{\mu_n r}{R} \right), \qquad \varphi_1(r) = \sum_{n=1}^{\infty} \frac{a\mu_n}{R} b_n J_0\left( \frac{\mu_n r}{R} \right).$$

The expansion coefficients are given by [5]

$$a_n = \frac{2}{R^2 J_1^2(\mu_n)} \int_0^R r\varphi_0(r) J_0\left( \frac{\mu_n r}{R} \right) dr,$$

$$b_n = \frac{2}{a\mu_n R J_1^2(\mu_n)} \int_0^R r\varphi_1(r) J_0\left( \frac{\mu_n r}{R} \right) dr.$$

Substituting this into (14.105) we obtain the solution of our problem. The solution given by (14.105) may be rewritten in the form

$$u(r, t) = \sum_{n=1}^{\infty} A_n J_0\left( \frac{\mu_n r}{R} \right) \sin \left( \frac{a\mu_n}{R} t + \varphi_n \right),$$

from which it is clear that the free radial oscillations of a membrane consist of an infinite number of harmonic oscillations whose frequencies are given by

$$\omega_n = \frac{a\mu_n}{R} = \frac{\mu_n}{R} \sqrt{\frac{T}{\rho}}.$$

The nodal lines for a circular membrane are determined from

$$J_0\left(\frac{\mu_n r}{R}\right) = 0.$$

from which it follows that the $n$-th overtone has $n$ nodal lines given by

$$r_1 = \frac{\mu_1}{\mu_n} R, \ r_2 = \frac{\mu_2}{\mu_n} R, \ \ldots, r_{n-1} = \frac{\mu_{n-1}}{\mu_n} R, \ \ r_n = R,$$

which take the form of concentric circles with the centre at the origin.

**Problems** (1) A uniform string fixed at its ends ($x = 0$ and $x = 1$) is initially in the form of a parabola which is symmetric about the perpendicular drawn through the point $x = \frac{1}{2}l$. Determine the displacement of all points of the string from the rectilinear position of equilibrium, assuming that the initial velocities are zero.

*Solution.*

$$u(x, t) = \frac{32h}{\pi^3} \sum_{k=0}^{\infty} \frac{\sin \dfrac{(2k+1)\pi x}{l} \cos \dfrac{(2k+1)\pi a t}{l}}{(2k+1)^3},$$

where $h = u(\frac{1}{2}l, 0)$.

(2) Investigate the forced transverse oscillations of a string fixed at one end ($x = 0$) and subjected to a displacement $A \sin \omega t$ at the other end ($x = l$).

*Solution.*

$$u(x, t) = \frac{A \sin \dfrac{\omega}{a} x \sin \omega t}{\sin \dfrac{\omega l}{a}} +$$

$$+ \frac{2Aa\omega}{l} \sum_{n=1}^{\infty} \frac{(-1)^{n-1}}{\omega^2 - \left(\dfrac{n\pi a}{l}\right)^2} \sin \frac{n\pi x}{l} \sin \frac{n\pi at}{l}.$$

(3) A rod is suspended vertically, and is constrained so that the displacement in all its cross-sections is zero. At time $t = 0$ the rod is freed, but remains fixed at the upper end. Investigate the forced oscillations of the rod under the action of gravity.

*Solution.*

$$u(x, t) = \frac{gx(2l - x)}{2a^2} - \frac{16gl^2}{\pi^3 a^2} \sum_{n=0}^{\infty} \frac{\sin \dfrac{(2n+1)\pi x}{l} \cos \dfrac{(2n+1)\pi at}{l}}{(2n+1)^3},$$

where $g$ is the gravitational acceleration.

(4) Find the natural oscillations of a uniform circular membrane of radius $R$ fixed along its periphery, if it is initially in the form of a paraboloid of revolution and the initial velocities are zero.

*Solution.*

$$u(r, t) = 8A \sum_{n=1}^{\infty} \frac{J_0\left(\mu_n \dfrac{r}{R}\right)}{\mu_n^3 J_1(\mu_n)} \cos \frac{a\mu_n t}{R},$$

where $\mu_1, \mu_2, \mu_3, \ldots$ are the positive roots of $J_0(\mu) = 0$ and $A = u(0, 0)$.

(5) A uniform square membrane whose form at the initial time $t = 0$ is described by $Axy(b - x)(b - y)$ where $A$ is a constant begins to oscillate with zero initial velocity. Investigate the free oscillations of the membrane if it is fixed along its edges.

*Solution.*

$$u(x, y, t) = \frac{64Ab^4}{\pi^6} \sum_{n, m=0}^{\infty} \frac{\sin \dfrac{(2n+1)\pi x}{b} \sin \dfrac{(2m+1)\pi y}{b}}{(2n+1)^3(2m+1)^3} \times$$

$$\times \cos \sqrt{(2n+1)^2 + (2m+1)^2} \, \frac{a\pi t}{b}.$$

Chapter 4

# EQUATIONS OF THE PARABOLIC TYPE

Equations of the parabolic type are most frequently encountered in the study of processes involving heat transfer and diffusion.

## § 15. First boundary value problem. Extremal theorem

**1. Formulation of the problem.** Let $\Omega$ be a finite region of the space $(x, y, z)$ and let $Q$ denote a cylinder in the space $(x, y, z, t)$ whose base is the region $\Omega$ and whose generators are parallel to the $t$-axis. Moreover, let $Q_T$ be a part of this cylinder which lies between the planes $t = 0$ and $t = T$, where $T > 0$. We shall denote by $\Gamma$ that part of the boundary of the cylinder $Q_T$ which consists of its lower base ($t = 0$) and its lateral surface.

Consider the following problem: it is required to find in the cylinder $Q_T$ the solution of the heat-transfer equation

$$\frac{\partial u}{\partial t} = a^2 \left( \frac{\partial^2 u}{\partial x^2} + \frac{\partial^2 u}{\partial y^2} + \frac{\partial^2 u}{\partial z^2} \right), \tag{15.1}$$

which satisfies the initial condition

$$u|_{t=0} = \varphi(x, y, z) \qquad ((x, y, z) \in \bar{\Omega}) \tag{15.2}$$

and the boundary condition

$$u|_S = \Psi(P, t) \qquad (t \in [0, T]), \tag{15.3}$$

where $S$ is the boundary of $\Omega$ and $P$ is a point on $S$. The functions $\varphi$ and $\Psi$ are continuous and the values for $T = 0$ are equal to the values of $\varphi$ on $S$. Determination of the solution of equation (15.1), subject to (15.2) and (15.3), is called *the first boundary value problem for the heat-transfer equation*.

*Theorem. The function $u(x, y, z, t)$ which satisfies the homogeneous heat-transfer equation* (15.1) *inside the cylinder $Q_T$ and is continuous* *right up to its boundary assumes its maximum and minimum values on* $\Gamma$, *i.e. either on* $t = 0$ *or on the lateral surface of the cylinder* $Q_T$. Since the minimum property can be reduced to the maximum property by changing the sign of $u(x, y, z, t)$, we shall confine our attention to the special case involving the maximum.

Let $M$ be the greatest value of $u(x, y, z, t)$ in the cylinder $\bar{D}_T$ and let $m$, be the smallest value of $u(x, y, z, t)$ on $\Gamma$. We shall suppose that there exists a solution $u(z, y, x, t)$ for which $M > m$, i.e. for which the maximum theorem is not valid. Suppose this function assumes the value $M$ at the point $(x_0, y_0, z_0, t_0)$ where $(x_0, y_0, z_0)$ belongs to $\Omega$ and $0 < t_0 \leqslant T$.

Consider the function

$$v(x, y, z, t) = u(x, y, z, t) +$$

$$+ \frac{M - m}{6d^2} [(x - x_0)^2 + (y - y_0)^2 + (z - z_0)^2],$$

where $d$ is the diameter of $\Omega$. On the lateral surface of the cylinder $D_T$ and on its lower base

$$v(x, y, z, t) \leqslant m + \frac{M - m}{6} = \frac{M}{6} + \frac{5m}{6} < M,$$

and $v(x_0, y_0, z_0, t_0) = M$. Consequently, neither $v(x, y, z, t)$ nor $u(x, y, z, t)$ assumes its maximum value either on the lateral surface of $D_T$ or on its lower base. Suppose that $v(x, y, z, t)$ assumes its maximum value at $(x_1, y_1, z_1, t_1)$ where $(x_1, y_1, z_1)$ lies inside $\Omega$ and $0 < t_1 \leqslant T$. The second derivatives $\partial^2 v/\partial x^2$, $\partial^2 v/\partial y^2$ and $\partial^2 v/\partial z^2$ are non-positive and $\partial v/\partial t \geqslant 0$ (if $t_1 < T$, then $\partial v/\partial t = 0$, whilst if $t_1 = T$, then $\partial v/\partial t \geqslant 0$), from which it follows that at the point $(x_1, y_1, z_1, t_1)$ we must have

$$\frac{\partial v}{\partial t} - a^2 \left( \frac{\partial^2 v}{\partial x^2} + \frac{\partial^2 v}{\partial y^2} + \frac{\partial^2 v}{\partial z^2} \right) \geqslant 0. \tag{*}$$

On the other hand,

$$\frac{\partial v}{\partial t} - a^2 \left( \frac{\partial^2 v}{\partial x^2} + \frac{\partial^2 v}{\partial y^2} + \frac{\partial^2 v}{\partial z^2} \right) =$$

$$= \frac{\partial u}{\partial t} - a^2 \left( \frac{\partial^2 u}{\partial x^2} + \frac{\partial^2 u}{\partial y^2} + \frac{\partial^2 u}{\partial z^2} \right) - a^2 \frac{M - m}{d^2} =$$

$$= - a^2 \frac{M - m}{d^2} < 0,$$

which contradicts (*). This proves the theorem.

It is a direct consequence of the above theorem that:

(1) *The solution of the first boundary-value problem defined by* (15.1)–(15.2) *is unique in the cylinder* $D_T$. In point of fact, if there were two such solutions $u_1$ and $u_2$, their difference $w = u_1 - u_2$ would satisfy the homogeneous equation (15.1) and would vanish both at $t = 0$ and on the surface $S$ of the region $\Omega$. This would mean, however, that in view of the above theorem $w$ would vanish identically in $\Omega$ for $0 \leqslant t \leqslant T$, i.e. $u_1 = u_2$.

(2) *The solution of the first boundary-value problem defined by* (15.1)–(15.2) *depends continuously on the right-hand side of the initial and boundary conditions.* In fact, if the difference functions which enter into the initial and boundary conditions, respectively, do not exceed in absolute magnitude a given positive number $\varepsilon$, the difference of the corresponding solutions $w = u_1 - u_2$, which is a solution of the homogeneous heat-transfer equation with small initial and boundary values would also be less than $\varepsilon$ throughout the cylinder $D_T$.

## 2. Solution of the first boundary value problem for the heat transfer equation.

The first boundary value problem for a rectangle $\bar{Q}$ $[0 \leqslant x \leqslant l, \, 0 \leqslant t \leqslant T]$ may be formulated as follows: *it is required to find a function* $u(x, t)$ *which is continuous in* $\bar{Q}$ *and satisfies in* $Q$ *the heat-transfer equation*

$$\frac{\partial u}{\partial t} = a^2 \frac{\partial^2 u}{\partial x^2} + f(x, t), \tag{15.4}$$

*the initial condition*

$$u|_{t=0} = \varphi(x) \qquad (0 \leqslant x \leqslant l) \tag{15.5}$$

*and the boundary conditions*

$$u|_{x=0} = \mu_1(t), \quad u|_{x=l} = \mu_2(t) \qquad (0 \leqslant t \leqslant T). \tag{15.5'}$$

It is assumed that the functions $f(x, t)$, $\varphi(x)$, $\mu_1(t)$ and $\mu_2(t)$ are continuous and $\varphi(0) = \mu_2(0)$.

We shall begin our study of the first boundary value problem (I) by considering the following simpler problem (I′): it is required to find in the rectangle a solution of the homogeneous equation

$$\frac{\partial u}{\partial t} = a^2 \frac{\partial^2 u}{\partial x^2}, \tag{15.6}$$

which satisfies the initial condition

$$u|_{t=0} = \varphi(x) \tag{15.7}$$

and the homogeneous boundary conditions

$$u|_{x=0} = 0, \quad u|_{x=l} = 0, \tag{15.8}$$

where $\varphi(x)$ is a piece-wise continuous first derivative and vanishes at $x = 0$ and $x = l$.

We shall now establish the existence of the solution of the boundary value problem (I′) for the rectangle $Q$ by the Fourier method.

We shall seek a special solution of equation (15.6) in the form

$$u(x, t) = T(t) X(x). \tag{15.9}$$

Substituting this into equation (15.6) we have

$$X(x)\, T'(t) = a^2 T(t)\, X''(x) \quad \text{or} \quad \frac{T'(t)}{a^2 T(t)} = \frac{X''(x)}{X(x)} = -\lambda,$$

from which we have the following two equations

$$T'(t) + a^2 \lambda T(t) = 0, \tag{15.10}$$

$$X''(x) + \lambda X(x) = 0. \tag{15.11}$$

In order to obtain nontrivial solutions $u(x, t)$ of the form given by (15.9) and satisfying the boundary conditions given by (15.8) we must find nontrivial solutions of (15.11) which satisfy the boundary condition

$$X(0) = 0, \quad X(l) = 0.$$

We thus arrive at the following eigenvalue problem:

$$X''(x) + \lambda X(x) = 0, \quad X(0) = 0, \quad X(l) = 0, \tag{15.12}$$

This has already been investigated in connection with the oscillations of a finite string, where it was shown that it was only for values of $\lambda$ given by

$$\lambda_n = \left(\frac{n\pi}{l}\right)^2 \qquad (n = 1, 2, 3, \ldots), \tag{15.13}$$

that their existed nontrivial solutions of (15.12) given by

$$X_n(x) = \sin\frac{n\pi x}{l}. \tag{15.14}$$

The solutions of (15.10) which correspond to the eigenvalues $\lambda = \lambda_n$ are

$$T_n(t) = a_n e^{-(n\pi a/l)^2 t}, \tag{15.15}$$

where $a_n$ are arbitrary constants.

Thus, all functions of the form

$$u_n(x, t) = T_n(t)\, X_n(x) = a_n e^{-(n\pi a/l)^2 t} \sin\frac{n\pi x}{l} \tag{15.16}$$

satisfy (15.6) and the boundary conditions (15.8).

Consider the series

$$u(x, t) = \sum_{n=1}^{\infty} a_n e^{-(n\pi a/l)^2 t} \sin\frac{n\pi x}{l}. \tag{15.17}$$

On substituting this into initial condition (15.7) we obtain

$$u(x, 0) = \varphi(x) = \sum_{n=1}^{\infty} a_n \sin\frac{n\pi x}{l}. \tag{15.18}$$

This is a Fourier expansion for the given function $\varphi(x)$ in the interval $(0, l)$. The coefficients $a_n$ are given by the well-known formula

$$a_n = \frac{2}{l} \int_0^l \varphi(x) \sin\frac{n\pi x}{l}\, dx. \tag{15.19}$$

Since, however, we have assumed that $\varphi(x)$ is continuous, has piece-wise continuous first derivative and vanishes at $x = 0$ and

$x = l$, it follows that equation (15.18), with $a_n$ given by (15.19), converges uniformly and absolutely for $\varphi(x)$, which is known from the theory of the trigonometric series. Since for $t \geqslant 0$ we have

$$0 < e^{-(n\pi a/l)^2 t} \leqslant 1,$$

it follows that the series (15.17) will also converge absolutely and uniformly for $t \geqslant 0$. Therefore, the function $u(x, t)$ defined by equation (15.17) is continuous for $0 \leqslant x \leqslant l$, $t \geqslant 0$ and satisfies the initial and boundary conditions. It remains to be shown that $u(x, t)$ satisfies equation (15.6) for $0 \leqslant x \leqslant l$, $t > 0$. To prove this, it is sufficient to show that the series obtained from (15.17) by differentiation term by term once with respect to $t$ and twice with respect to $x$ are also absolutely and uniformly convergent for $0 < x \leqslant l$, $t > 0$, and provided $n$ is large enough

$$0 < \frac{n^2\pi^2 a^2}{l^2} e^{-(n\pi a/l)^2 t} < 1, \quad 0 < \frac{n^2\pi^2}{l^2} e^{-(n\pi a/l)^2 t} < 1,$$

The existence of continuous derivatives of any order with respect to $x$ and $t$ of the function $u(x, t)$ can be established in a similar way for $0 \leqslant x \leqslant l$, $t > 0$.

The uniqueness of the solution of the problem (I′) and the continuous dependence of $\varphi(x)$ on the initial conditions has been established as a consequence of the above extremal theorem. This problem is, therefore, formulated correctly for $t > 0$ if the initial condition refers to $t = 0$.

*Remarks.* Suppose that the problem (I′) has a solution for negative $t$. This solution must, therefore, be capable of any change for any small negative $t$ by varying any small function $\varphi(x)$ and its derivatives up to a given arbitrary order $k$. For this it is sufficient to add to the solution an arbitrary term of (15.17) of high enough number with an arbitrarily small constant factor. Hence it follows that the problem (I′) is formulated incorrectly for negative $t$. If the initial condition refers to $t = 0$.

Problem (I″). It is required to find in the rectangle $Q$ the solution of the homogeneous equation

$$\frac{\partial u}{\partial t} = a^2 \frac{\partial^2 u}{\partial x^2} + f(x, t), \tag{15.20}$$

which satisfies the initial condition

$$u|_{t=0} = 0 \tag{15.21}$$

and the homogeneous boundary conditions

$$u|_{x=0} = 0, \quad u|_{x=l} = 0. \tag{15.22}$$

It is assumed that the continuous function $f(x, t)$ has piecewise continuous first derivative and that for all $t > 0$ we have $(f0, t) = = f(l, t) = 0$.

We shall seek the solution $u(x, t)$ of (I″) in the form of the Fourier series

$$u(x, t) = \sum_{n=1}^{\infty} T_n(t) \sin \frac{n\pi x}{l} \tag{15.23}$$

where $T_N(t)$ are the eigenfunctions of problem (15.12). We can expand $f(x, t)$ into the Fourier series

$$f(x, t) = \sum_{n=1}^{\infty} f_n(t) \sin \frac{n\pi x}{l}, \tag{15.24}$$

where

$$f_n(t) = \frac{2}{l} \int_0^l f(x, t) \sin \frac{n\pi x}{l} \, dx. \tag{15.25}$$

Substitution of (15.23) into (15.20) yields, in view of (15.24)

$$\sum_{n=1}^{\infty} \left[ T_n'(t) + \left( \frac{an\pi}{l} \right)^2 T_n(t) - f_n(t) \right] \sin \frac{n\pi x}{l} = 0.$$

and hence

$$T_n'(t) + \left( \frac{n\pi a}{l} \right)^2 T_n(t) = f_n(t) \qquad (n = 1, 2, 3, \ldots). \tag{15.26}$$

Using the initial condition for $u(x, t)$

$$u(x, 0) = \sum_{n=1}^{\infty} T_n(0) \sin \frac{n\pi x}{l} = 0,$$

we obtain the initial condition for $T_n(t)$

$$T_n(0) = 0 \qquad (n = 1, 2, 3, \ldots). \tag{15.27}$$

The solution of (15.26) subject to the initial condition (15.27) is of the form

$$T_n(t) = \int_0^t e^{-(n\pi a/l)^2(t-\tau)} f_n(\tau) \, d\tau. \tag{15.28}$$

Substituting this expression into (15.23) we obtain the solution of (I″) in the form

$$u(x, t) = \sum_{n=1}^{\infty} \left[ \int_0^t e^{-(n\pi a/l)^2(t-\tau)} f_n(\tau) \, d\tau \right] \sin \frac{n\pi x}{l}. \tag{15.29}$$

*Remarks.* If the initial conditions are inhomogeneous we must add to (15.29) the solution of the homogeneous heat-transfer equation with given boundary condition $u(x, 0) = \varphi(x)$ and homogeneous boundary conditions $u(0, t) = 0$, $u(l, t) = 0$.

Let us return now to the general form of the first boundary value problem (I). We shall introduce a new unknown function $v(x, t)$ by substituting

$$u(x, t) = v(x, t) + w(x, t),$$

where

$$w(x, t) = \mu_1(t) + [\mu_2(t) - \mu_1(t)] \frac{x}{l}.$$

The function $v(x, t)$ will be determined as the solution of

$$\frac{\partial v}{\partial t} = a^2 \frac{\partial^2 v}{\partial x^2} + \bar{f}(x, t), \tag{15.30}$$

where

$$\bar{f}(x, t) = f(x, t) - w_t(x, t),$$

subject to the initial conditions

$$v(x, 0) = \varphi(x) - w(x, 0) \tag{15.31}$$

and the boundary conditions

$$v(0, t) = u(0, t) - w(0, t) = 0,$$
$$v(l, t) = u(l, t) - w(l, t) = 0.$$

(15.32)

The solution of problem (I) has thus been reduced to the solution of the problem defined by (15.30)–(15.32) which was solved above.

**Problems.** (1) The initial temperature at any point in a uniform sphere of radius $R$ with center at the origin is a function of only the distance $r$ of this point from the origin. The outer surface of the sphere is maintained at zero temperature. Determine the temperature distribution inside the sphere for times $t > 0$.
*Answer:*

$$u(r, t) = \frac{2}{Rr} \sum_{n=1}^{\infty} e^{-(n\pi a/R)^2 t} \sin \frac{n\pi r}{R} \int_0^R \rho\varphi(\rho) \sin \frac{n\pi\rho}{R} \, d\rho,$$

where $\varphi(r)$ is the initial temperature of the sphere.
(2) A thin uniform rod of length $l$ whose lateral surface is thermally insulated is at a known initial temperature. The end $x = 0$ of the rod is maintained at zero temperature, while at $x = l$ there is heat-transfer between the rod and the surrounding medium, which is at zero temperature. Determine the temperature of the rod at time $t > 0$.
*Answer:*

$$u(x, t) = \frac{2}{l} \sum_{n=1}^{\infty} \frac{p^2 + \mu_n^2}{p(p+1) + \mu_n^2} e^{-(\mu_n a/l)^2 t} \sin \frac{\mu_n x}{R} \int_0^l \varphi(\xi) \sin \frac{\mu_n \xi}{l} \, d\xi,$$

where $\mu_1, \mu_2, \mu_3, \ldots$ are the positive roots of the equation

$$\tan \mu = -\frac{\mu}{p}, \quad p = Hl > 0.$$

(3) Find the temperature distribution inside an infinite circular cylinder of radius $R$ whose initial temperature is

$$u|_{t=0} = u_0 \left( 1 - \frac{r^2}{R^2} \right),$$

and whose lateral surface is maintained at zero temperature. *Answer*:

$$u(r, t) = 8u_0 \sum_{u=1}^{\infty} \frac{J_0\left(\dfrac{\mu_n r}{R}\right)}{\mu_n^3 J_1(\mu_n)} e^{-(\mu_n a/R)^2 t}.$$

### § 16. Cauchy's problem

**1. Formulation of Cauchy's problem.** It is required to find the function $u(x, t)$ $(t > 0, -\infty < x < \infty)$ which satisfies the heat-transfer equation

$$\frac{\partial u}{\partial t} = a^2 \frac{\partial^2 u}{\partial x^2} \qquad (16.1)$$

subject to the initial condition

$$u|_{t=0} = \varphi(x) \qquad (-\infty < x < \infty), \qquad (16.2)$$

where $\varphi(x)$ is continuous and bounded.

**2. Uniqueness of solution.** We shall prove the uniqueness of the solution of Cauchy's problem assuming that the solution $u(x, t)$ is bounded throughout, i.e. there exists a number $M$ such that $|u(x, t)| < M$ for all $-\infty < x < \infty$ and any $t \geqslant 0$.

Suppose that $u_1(x, t)$ and $u_2(x, t)$ are two solutions of (16.1) which satisfy the same initial condition (16.2). The difference $\omega(x, t) = u_1(x, t) - u_2(x, y)$ will satisfy (16.1) and the initial condition

$$\omega|_{t=0} = 0.$$

Moreover, $\omega(x, t)$ is bounded in the entire region

$$|\omega(x, t)| \leqslant |u_1(x, t)| + |u_2(x, t)| \leqslant 2M.$$

The extremal theorem established in the preceding section cannot be directly employed here because $\omega(x, t)$ nowhere reaches its maximum and minimum values. In order to employ this theorem consider the finite region

$$|x| \leqslant L, \quad 0 \leqslant t \leqslant T. \qquad (16.3)$$

Let us take the solution of the heat-transfer condition (16.1).

$$v(x, t) = \frac{4M}{L^2}\left(\frac{x^2}{2} + a^2 t\right),$$

It is readily seen that

$$v(x, 0) \geqslant \omega(x, 0) = 0,$$
$$v(\pm L, t) \geqslant 2M \geqslant |\omega(\pm L, t)|.$$

and if we apply the extremal theorem to the difference between the functions $v(x, t)$ and $\pm \omega(x, t)$ in the region defined by (16.3) we have

$$v(x, t) - \omega(x, t) \geqslant 0, \quad v(x, t) + \omega(x, t) \geqslant 0,$$

whence

$$-v(x, t) \leqslant \omega(x, t) \leqslant v(x, t)$$

or

$$|\omega(x, t)| \leqslant v(x, t) = \frac{4M}{L^2}\left(\frac{x^2}{2} + a^2 t\right).$$

If we allow $x$ and $t$ to assume the fixed values $(x_0, t_0)$ and choose $L$ to be large enough, we obtain

$$|\omega(x_0, t_0)| < \varepsilon,$$

and hence, in view of the fact that $\varepsilon$ and $(x_0, t_0)$ are arbitrary, it follows that

$$\omega(x, t) \equiv 0.$$

3. **Existence of the solution of Cauchy's problem.** To begin with, we shall derive special solutions of (16.1) in the form

$$u(x, t) = T(t) X(x). \tag{16.4}$$

Substituting this into (16.1) and separating the variables we obtain

$$\frac{T'(t)}{a^2 T(t)} = \frac{X''(x)}{X(x)} = -\lambda^2,$$

where $\lambda^2$ is a constant. Hence,

$$T'(t) + a^2\lambda^2 T(t) = 0, \quad X''(x) + \lambda^2 X(x) = 0,$$

and if we set the factor in the expression for $T(t)$ equal to unity, we have

$$T(t) = e^{-a^2\lambda^2 t}, \quad X(x) = A\cos\lambda x + B\sin\lambda x;$$

The constants $A$ and $B$ may depend on $\lambda$. Since there are no boundary conditions the parameter $\lambda$ is arbitrary.

From equation (16.4) we find that

$$u_\lambda(x, t) = e^{-a^2\lambda^2 t}[A(\lambda)\cos\lambda x + B(\lambda)\sin\lambda x] \tag{16.5}$$

is a special solution of (16.1) for any $A(\lambda)$ and $B(\lambda)$. Integrating (16.5) with respect to $\lambda$ we obtain the following solution of (16.1)

$$u(x, t) = \int_{-\infty}^{\infty} e^{-a^2\lambda^2 t}[A(\lambda)\cos\lambda x + B(\lambda)\sin\lambda x]\,d\lambda, \tag{16.6}$$

provided this integral converges uniformly and can be differentiated under the integral sign once with respect to $t$ and twice with respect to $x$.

We shall choose $A(\lambda)$ and $B(\lambda)$ so as to satisfy the initial condition (16.2). If we set $t = 0$ in (16.6), using (16.2), we obtain

$$\varphi(x) = \int_{-\infty}^{\infty} [A(\lambda)\cos\lambda x + B(\lambda)\sin\lambda x]\,d\lambda. \tag{16.7}$$

Comparison of this integral with the Fourier integral for $\varphi(x)$

$$\varphi(x) = \frac{1}{2\pi} \int_{-\infty}^{\infty} d\lambda \int_{-\infty}^{\infty} \varphi(\xi)\cos\lambda(\xi - x)\,d\xi =$$

$$= \frac{1}{2\pi} \int_{-\infty}^{\infty} \left[\cos\lambda x \int_{-\infty}^{\infty} \varphi(\xi)\cos\lambda\xi\,d\xi + \sin\lambda x \int_{-\infty}^{\infty} \varphi(\xi)\sin\lambda\xi\,d\xi\right]d\lambda,$$

will show that (16.7) can be satisfied if

$$A(\lambda) = \frac{1}{2\pi} \int\limits_{-\infty}^{\infty} \varphi(\xi) \cos \lambda \xi \, d\xi,$$

$$B(\lambda) = \frac{1}{2\pi} \int\limits_{-\infty}^{\infty} \varphi(\xi) \sin \lambda \xi \, d\xi.$$

(16.8)

Substituting (16.8) into (16.6) we have

$$u(x, t) = \frac{1}{2\pi} \int\limits_{-\infty}^{\infty} d\lambda \int\limits_{-\infty}^{\infty} \varphi(\xi) e^{-a^2\lambda^2 t} \cos \lambda(\xi - x) \, d\xi =$$

$$= \frac{1}{\pi} \int\limits_{0}^{\infty} d\lambda \int\limits_{-\infty}^{\infty} \varphi(\xi) e^{-a^2\lambda^2 t} \cos \lambda(\xi - x) \, d\xi.$$

If we change the order of integration and use the result

$$\int\limits_{0}^{\infty} e^{-a^2\lambda^2} \cos \beta\lambda \, d\lambda = \frac{\sqrt{\pi}}{2\alpha} e^{-(\beta^2/4\alpha^2)},$$

we easily find that

$$u(x, t) = \int\limits_{-\infty}^{\infty} \varphi(\xi) \frac{1}{2a\sqrt{\pi t}} e^{-[(\xi x)^2/4a^2 t]} \, d\xi.$$

(16.9)

It is readily seen that the function

$$F(x, t; \xi) = \frac{1}{2a\sqrt{\pi t}} e^{-[(\xi - x)^2/4a^2 t]},$$

(16.10)

looked upon as a function of $x$ and $t$, is a solution of (16.1); it is called the *fundamental solution* of the heat-transfer equation (16.1). We shall show that for any continuous bounded function $\varphi(x)$ the function (16.9) satisfies the heat-transfer equation (16.1). For this it will be sufficient to show that the integral (16.9) and integrals obtained by differentiating formulas under the integral sign with respect to $x$ and $t$ any number of times will converge uniformly in any rectangle $-l \leqslant x \leqslant l$, $t_0 \leqslant t \leqslant T$ where $t_0 > 0$. In fact, if we differentiate (16.9) several times with respect to $x$ and $t$ we obtain a sum of integrals and it may be shown that each integral converges uniformly. After differentiation under the integral sign we can separate out a factor $\xi - x$ raised to a positive power which remains under the integral sign and a factor $t$ raised to a certain power which can be taken out from under the integral sign. We thus obtain a sum of integrals of the form

$$I = \frac{1}{t^k} \int\limits_{-\infty}^{\infty} \varphi(\xi)(\xi - x)^m e^{-[(\xi-x)^2/4a^2t]} d\xi. \tag{16.11}$$

Substituting

$$\alpha = \frac{\xi - x}{2a\sqrt{t}} \qquad (t > 0),$$

we can transform (16.11) to

$$I = (2a)^{m+1} t^{(m+1/2)-k} \int\limits_{-\infty}^{\infty} \varphi(x + 2a\alpha\sqrt{t}) \alpha^m e^{-\alpha^2} d\alpha.$$

Hence, it is readily seen that this integral converges uniformly for $t \geqslant t_0 > 0$ since the function $M|\alpha|^m e^{-\alpha^2}$, where

$$|\varphi(x + 2a\alpha\sqrt{t})| < M,$$

which is integrable in the interval $(-\infty, \infty)$ is a majorant of the integrand in the above expression.

We have thus proved that the function $u(x, t)$, as defined by (16.9), is continuous and possesses derivatives of any order with respect to $x$ and $t$ for $t > 0$. Since the integrand satisfies (16.1) for $t > 0$, it follows that $u(x, t)$ itself satisfies this equation for $t > 0$.

We shall now show that (16.9) satisfies the initial condition (16.2), i.e.

$$\lim_{t \to 0} u(x, t) = \varphi(x)$$

for any $x$ in the range $(-\infty, \infty)$. Substituting

$$\alpha = \frac{\xi - x}{2a\sqrt{t}} \qquad (t > 0).$$

into (16.9) we obtain

$$u(x, t) = \frac{1}{\sqrt{\pi}} \int\limits_{-\infty}^{\infty} \varphi(x + 2a\alpha\sqrt{t}) e^{-\alpha^2} d\alpha. \tag{16.12}$$

It is readily shown from this that $u(x, t)$ must be bounded in $-\infty < x < \infty$ and $t > 0$ if $|\varphi(x)| < M$ for all $x$. In fact,

$$|u(x, t)| \leqslant \frac{1}{\sqrt{\pi}} \int\limits_{-\infty}^{\infty} |\varphi(x + 2a\alpha\sqrt{t})| e^{-\alpha^2} d\alpha \leqslant$$

$$\leqslant \frac{M}{\sqrt{\pi}} \int\limits_{-\infty}^{\infty} e^{-\alpha^2} d\alpha = M,$$

since

$$\frac{1}{\sqrt{\pi}} \int\limits_{-\infty}^{\infty} e^{-\alpha^2} d\alpha = 1. \tag{16.13}$$

Multiplying (16.13) by $\varphi(x)$ and subtracting from (16.12) we obtain

$$u(x, t) - \varphi(x) = \frac{1}{\sqrt{\pi}} \int\limits_{-\infty}^{\infty} [\varphi(x + 2a\alpha\sqrt{t}) - \varphi(x)] e^{-\alpha^2} d\alpha,$$

and hence

$$|u(x, t) - \varphi(x)| \leqslant \frac{1}{\sqrt{\pi}} \int\limits_{-\infty}^{\infty} |\varphi(x + 2a\alpha\sqrt{t}) - \varphi(x)| e^{-\alpha^2} d\alpha. \tag{16.14}$$

Since $\varphi(x)$ is bounded for any $x$, $t$ and $\alpha$ we have

$$|\varphi(x + 2a\alpha\sqrt{t}) - \varphi(x)| \leqslant 2M. \tag{16.15}$$

Let $\varepsilon > 0$ be an arbitrarily small number. Since the integral in (16.13) converges, we can find a fixed large positive number $N$ such that

$$\frac{2M}{\sqrt{\pi}} \int\limits_{-\infty}^{-N} e^{-\alpha^2} d\alpha \leqslant \frac{\varepsilon}{3}, \quad \frac{2M}{\sqrt{\pi}} \int\limits_{N}^{\infty} e^{-\alpha^2} d\alpha \leqslant \frac{\varepsilon}{3}. \tag{16.16}$$

If we divide the range of integration into the three parts

$$(-\infty, -N), \quad (-N, N), \quad (N, \infty)$$

and use (16.15) and (16.16) we have from (16.14)

$$|u(x, t) - \varphi(x)| \leqslant \frac{2\varepsilon}{3} +$$

$$+ \frac{1}{\sqrt{\pi}} \int\limits_{-N}^{N} |\varphi(x + 2a\alpha\sqrt{t}) - \varphi(x)| e^{-\alpha^2} d\alpha.$$

Since $\varphi(x)$ is continuous for all $t$, which are close enough to zero, and for $|\alpha| \leqslant N$, we have

$$|\varphi(x + 2a\alpha\sqrt{t}) - \varphi(x)| \leqslant \frac{\varepsilon}{3},$$

which yields

$$|u(x, t) - \varphi(x)| \leqslant \frac{2\varepsilon}{3} + \frac{\varepsilon}{3} \frac{1}{\sqrt{\pi}} \int\limits_{-N}^{N} e^{-\alpha^2} d\alpha,$$

and

$$|u(x, t) - \varphi(x)| \leqslant \frac{2\varepsilon}{3} + \frac{\varepsilon}{3} \frac{1}{\sqrt{\pi}} \int\limits_{-\infty}^{\infty} e^{-\alpha^2} d\alpha,$$

i.e. from (16.13) we have $|u(x, t) - \varphi(x)| < \varepsilon$ for all $t$ sufficiently close to zero and all $x$ and since $\varepsilon > 0$ is arbitrary, it follows that

$$\lim_{t \to 0} u(x, t) = \varphi(x),$$

which was to be proved.

**4. Continuous dependence of the solution of Cauchy's problem on the initial function.** Let $u(x, t)$ be the solution of (16.1) which satisfies the initial condition (16.2) and suppose that $\bar{u}(x, t)$ is a solution of some equation which satisfies the initial condition

$$\bar{u}|_{t=0} = \bar{\varphi}(x). \tag{16.17}$$

If $|\bar{\varphi}(x) - \varphi(x)| < \varepsilon$ for all $x$ in the range $(-\infty, \infty)$, then $|\bar{u}(x, t) - u(x, t)| < \varepsilon$ for any $x$ and $t > 0$. In fact, the solutions

of (16.1) which satisfy (16.2) and (16.17), respectively, are given
by (16.9). Their difference is given by

$$\bar{u}(x, t) - u(x, t) = \int\limits_{-\infty}^{\infty} [\bar{\varphi}(\xi) - \varphi(\xi)] \, \frac{1}{2a\sqrt{\pi t}} \, e^{-[(x-\xi)^2/4a^2 t]} \, d\xi,$$

and hence

$$|\bar{u}(x, t) - u(x, t)| \leqslant \frac{\varepsilon}{2a\sqrt{\pi t}} \int\limits_{-\infty}^{\infty} e^{-[(x-\xi)^2/4a^2 t]} \, d\xi$$

or substituting

$$\alpha = \frac{\xi - x}{2a\sqrt{t}} \, ,$$

we obtain

$$|\bar{u}(x, t) - u(x, t)| \leqslant \varepsilon \, \frac{1}{\sqrt{\pi}} \int\limits_{-\infty}^{\infty} e^{-\alpha^2} \, d\alpha = \varepsilon,$$

which was to be proved.

This follows from (16.9) that the heat propagates instantaneously
along the rod. In fact, suppose that the initial temperature $\varphi(x)$
is positive for $\alpha \leqslant x \leqslant \beta$ and is zero outside this interval. The
subsequent temperature distribution is then given by

$$u(x, t) = \int\limits_{\alpha}^{\beta} \varphi(\xi) \, \frac{1}{2a\sqrt{\pi t}} \, e^{-[(\xi-x)^2/4a^2 t]} \, d\xi,$$

from which it is evident that for times $t > 0$ as small as desired
and for $x$ as large as desired, we have $u(x, t)$ greater than zero.
This is explained by the lack of precision in the theoretical assumptions upon which the heat-transfer theory is based.

We must note one further important fact. The solution of the
problem satisfied by (16.1)–(16.2) (Cauchy's problem) is a function
which is continuously differentiable any number of times with
respect to $x$ and $t$ independently of whether the function $\varphi(x)$
possesses derivatives or not. This distinguishes the homogeneous
heat-transfer equation from, for example, the equation for the
oscillations of a string.

Let us consider now the physical significance of the fundamental solution (16.10) of the homogeneous heat-transfer equation (16.1).

Consider a small element $(x_0 - h, x_0 + h)$ of the rod and suppose that the function $\varphi(x)$ which represents the initial temperature distribution vanishes outside this interval but has a constant value equal to $U_0$ inside this interval. Physically, this means that at the initial time we communicated an amount of heat $Q = 2hc\rho U_0$ to this element which gave rise to an increase in the temperature of the rod in this segment by $U_0$. The subsequent temperature distribution in the rod is given by (16.9) which, in the present case, takes the form

$$u(x, t) = \int_{x_0-h}^{x_0+h} U_0 \frac{1}{2a\sqrt{\pi t}} e^{-[(\xi-x)^2/4a^2 t]} d\xi =$$

$$= \frac{Q}{c\rho 2a\sqrt{\pi t}} \frac{1}{2h} \int_{x_0-h}^{x_0+h} e^{-[(\xi-x)^2/4a^2 t]} d\xi.$$

If we now let $h$ tend to zero, i.e. if we suppose that the heat $Q$ is communicated to a continuously decreasing segment of the rod and in the limit is confined to the point $x = x_0$, we arrive at the concept of an *instantaneous point source of heat of strength $Q$ which lies at the point $x = x_0$ at time $t = 0$*. An instantaneous point source of heat of this kind gives rise to a temperature distribution in the rod which is described by

$$\lim_{h\to 0} \frac{Q}{c\rho 2a\sqrt{\pi t}} \frac{1}{2h} \int_{x_0-h}^{x_0+h} e^{-[(\xi-x)^2/4a^2 t]} d\xi, \qquad (16.18)$$

and if we use the mean value theorem we have

$$\frac{1}{2h} \int_{x_0-h}^{x_0+h} e^{-[(\xi-x)^2/4a^2 t]} d\xi = e^{-[(\xi_0-x)^2/4a^2 t]},$$

where $x_0 - h < \xi_0 < x_0 + h$ and since $\xi_0 \to x_0$ for $h \to 0$, the

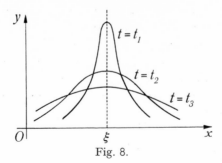

Fig. 8.

expression given by (16.18) becomes

$$\frac{Q}{c\rho}\;\frac{1}{2a\sqrt{\pi t}}\;e^{-[(x_0-x)^2/4a^2t]}.$$

It follows that *the fundamental solution* (15.10) *gives the temperature distribution which is produced by an instantaneous point source of heat of strength* $Q = c\rho$ *which lies at the point* $x = \xi$ *at time* $t = 0$. Figure 8 shows plots of the fundamental solution

$$F(x,\,t;\,\xi) = \frac{1}{2a\sqrt{\pi t}}\,e^{-[(\xi-x)^2/4a^2t]} \tag{16.10}$$

for given $\xi$ as a function of $x$ and different times $0<t_1<t_2<t_3<\dots$. The area under each of these curves is

$$\int_{-\infty}^{\infty} \frac{1}{2a\sqrt{\pi t}}\,e^{-[(\xi-x)^2/4a^2t]}d\xi = \frac{1}{\sqrt{\pi}}\int_{-\infty}^{\infty} e^{-\alpha^2}d\alpha = 1.$$

This means that the amount of heat $Q = c\rho$ in the rod is independent of time. It is evident from the graph that practically the entire area under the curve as described by (16.10) lies above $(\xi - \varepsilon,\ \xi + \varepsilon)$ where $\varepsilon$ is as small as desired provided only $t > 0$ is small enough. The magnitude of this area multiplied by $c\rho$ is equal to the amount of heat introduced at the initial time. Therefore, for small $t > 0$ practically the entire heat is concentrated in the immediate vicinity of $x = \xi$. It follows from the above description that at time $t = 0$ the entire heat is at $x = \xi$, i.e. we have an instantaneous point source of heat.

It is now quite easy to give a physical interpretation of (16.9). In fact, in order to raise the cross section $x = \xi$ of the rod to a temperature $\varphi(\xi)$ at the initial instant of time, we must distribute an amount of heat $dQ = c\rho\varphi(\xi)\,d\xi$ in the immediate vicinity of $\xi$, i.e. place an instantaneous point source of heat $dQ$ at the point $\xi$. The temperature distribution produced by this point source will, in view of (16.10) be

$$\varphi(\xi)\,d\xi\,\frac{1}{2a\sqrt{\pi t}}\,e^{-[(\xi-x)^2/4a^2t]}.$$

The overall result of imposing an initial temperature distribution $\varphi(\xi)$ is obtained by integrating this expression and this yields the solution given by (16.9), i.e.

$$u(x,t) = \int\limits_{-\infty}^{\infty} \varphi(\xi)\cdot\frac{1}{2a\sqrt{\pi t}}\,e^{-[(\xi-x)^2/4a^2t]}\,d\xi.$$

The heat-transfer equation

$$\frac{\partial u}{\partial t} = a^2\left(\frac{\partial^2 u}{\partial x^2} + \frac{\partial^2 u}{\partial y^2} + \frac{\partial^2 u}{\partial z^2}\right). \tag{16.19}$$

can be dealt with in a similar way. The solution of this equation which satisfies the boundary condition

$$u|_{t=0} = \varphi(x,y,z),$$

is given by

$$u(x,y,z,t) =$$
$$= \int\limits_{-\infty}^{\infty}\int\limits_{-\infty}^{\infty}\int\limits_{-\infty}^{\infty} \varphi(\xi,\eta,\zeta)\,\frac{1}{(2a\sqrt{\pi t})^3}\,e^{-[(\xi-x)^2+(\eta-y)^2+(\zeta-z)^2]/4a^2t}\,d\xi\,d\eta\,d\zeta.$$

**Problem.** Show that the inhomogeneous equation

$$\frac{\partial u}{\partial t} = a^2\,\frac{\partial^2 u}{\partial x^2} + f(x,t)$$

subject to the initial condition

$$u|_{t=0} = 0$$

has a solution of the form

$$u(x, t) = \int_0^t \int_{-\infty}^\infty \frac{f(\xi, \tau)}{2a\sqrt{\pi(t - \tau)}} \, e^{-(\xi-x)^2/[4a^2(t-\tau)]} d\xi \, d\tau.$$

*Hint.* Use the method described in § 11 in connection with the inhomogeneous wave equation.

Chapter 5

# EQUATIONS OF THE ELLIPTIC TYPE

### § 17. Laplace equation

Problems involving stationary phenomena, i.e. phenomena which are independent of time, can be reduced to equations of the elliptic type. The simplest equation of this type is the Laplace equation

$$\frac{\partial^2 u}{\partial x^2} + \frac{\partial^2 u}{\partial y^2} + \frac{\partial^2 u}{\partial z^2} = 0. \tag{17.1}$$

We have seen in § 5 that the steady-state temperature distribution in a uniform isotropic body $u(x, y, z)$ is a solution of this equation. The gravitational and electrostatic potentials are also solutions of the Laplace equation at points at which there are no masses and charges.

The function $u(x, y, z)$ is referred to as *harmonic in a finite domain D* if it has continuous derivatives up to the second order in this domain and satisfies the Laplace equations at all points in $D$.

The function $u(x, y, z)$ is called *harmonic in an infinite domain D* if in this domain it has continuous derivatives up to the second order, satisfies the Laplace equations at all points of $D$ and tends uniformly to zero as the point $M(x, y, z)$ tends to infinity (the function $u(M) \to 0$ as $M \to \infty$ if for any given positive $\varepsilon$ it is possible to find a positive number $A$ such that $|u(M)| < \varepsilon$ for $r \geqslant A$, where $r$ is the distance of $M$ from the origin.

We shall always assume that the boundary of the domain $D$ consists of a finite number of closed surfaces.

**Lemma 1.** *The function*

$$\frac{1}{r} = \frac{1}{\sqrt{(x - x_0)^2 + (y - y_0)^2 + (z - z_0)^2}}$$

*is harmonic in any domain not including the point* $(x_0, y_0, z_0)$.

This limit can be established by direct verification. The function $u = 1/r$ is called the *fundamental solution of the Laplace equation* (17.1).

Similarly, the function

$$u = \ln \frac{1}{r} = \ln \frac{1}{\sqrt{(x - x_0)^2 + (y - y_0)^2}}$$

is called the fundamental solution of the two-dimensional Laplace equation

$$\frac{\partial^2 u}{\partial x^2} + \frac{\partial^2 u}{\partial y^2} = 0.$$

Before we proceed to the study of the properties of harmonic functions we must establish a number of formulae which will be useful in the ensuing analysis.

## § 18. Green's formula.
### Integral representation of an arbitrary function

Let $D$ be a finite domain of three-dimensional space bounded by a piecewise smooth orientable surface $S$ and let the functions $P(x, y, z)$, $Q(x, y, z)$, $R(x, y, z)$ have continuous and bounded first-order derivatives in $D$. Under these conditions we can use the Gauss theorem

$$\iiint\limits_D \left( \frac{\partial P}{\partial x} + \frac{\partial Q}{\partial y} + \frac{\partial R}{\partial z} \right) d\tau =$$

$$= \iint\limits_S [P \cos (nx) + Q \cos (ny) + R \cos (nz)] \, dS, \qquad (18.1)$$

where $n$ is the outward normal to the surface $S$.

We will begin by proving Green's formula. Let $u(x, y, z)$ and $v(x, y, z)$ and their first-order partial derivatives be continuous in $D$ right up to $S$, and let the second-order partial derivatives inside $D$ be continuous and bounded. Substituting

$$P = u \frac{\partial v}{\partial x}, \quad Q = u \frac{\partial v}{\partial y}, \quad R = u \frac{\partial v}{\partial z}$$

and using (18.1) we obtain Green's first formula

$$\iiint\limits_{D} \left( \frac{\partial u}{\partial x} \frac{\partial v}{\partial x} + \frac{\partial u}{\partial y} \frac{\partial v}{\partial y} + \frac{\partial u}{\partial z} \frac{\partial v}{\partial z} \right) d\tau =$$

$$= \iint\limits_{S} u \frac{\partial v}{\partial n} dS - \iiint\limits_{D} u \Delta v \, d\tau. \qquad (18.2)$$

If we interchange $u$ and $v$ in (18.2), we obtain

$$\iiint\limits_{D} \left( \frac{\partial u}{\partial x} \frac{\partial v}{\partial x} + \frac{\partial u}{\partial y} \frac{\partial v}{\partial y} + \frac{\partial u}{\partial z} \frac{\partial v}{\partial z} \right) d\tau =$$

$$= \iint\limits_{S} v \frac{\partial u}{\partial n} dS - \iiint\limits_{D} v \Delta u \, d\tau. \qquad (18.3)$$

and if we subtract (18.2) from (18.3) we obtain Green's second formula

$$\iiint\limits_{D} (u \Delta v - v \Delta u) \, d\tau = \iint\limits_{S} \left( u \frac{\partial v}{\partial n} - v \frac{\partial u}{\partial n} \right) dS. \qquad (18.4)$$

*Remarks.* The domain $D$ may be bounded by a number of closed surfaces. Green's formulae are still valid under these conditions but the surface integrals must be evaluated over all surfaces bounding $D$. We note that the normal $n$ which is outward with respect to $D$ will on the surfaces bounding this region internally be directed inward.

**Lemma 2.** *If a function $u(x, y, z)$ is continuous, has continuous first- and second-order derivatives throughout $D$, while the first derivatives are continuous up to the boundary $S$ whilst the second derivatives are continuous inside the domain, then*

$$u(x_0, y_0, z_0) =$$

$$= \frac{1}{4\pi} \iint\limits_{S} \left( \frac{1}{r} \frac{\partial u}{\partial n} - u \frac{\partial \frac{1}{r}}{\partial n} \right) dS - \frac{1}{4\pi} \iiint\limits_{D} \frac{\Delta u}{r} d\tau, \qquad (18.5)$$

where $r = \sqrt{(x - x_0)^2 + (y - y_0)^2 + (z - z_0)^2}$ is the distance of the fixed point $M_0(x_0, y_0, z_0)$ lying inside $D$ from the running point $M(x, y, z)$ and $n$ is the outward normal to $S$.

*Proof.* We shall suppose, to start with, that the function $u$ has continuous second-order derivatives right up to the surface $S$. Consider the function $v = 1/r$. Since this function becomes infinite when $M$ coincides with $M_0$, we cannot apply Green's formula to the entire domain $D$. Let us exclude from $D$ a sphere centered at the point $M_0$ having a small radius $\rho$ and let $D_\rho$ represent the remaining part of $D$ and $\sigma_0$ represent the surface of the sphere. In $D_\rho$ the functions $u$ and $v = 1/r$ have the required continuity properties and Green's formula (18.4) is valid in this region. Since $v = 1/r$ is a harmonic function in $D_\rho$, we have

$$\iiint\limits_{D_\rho} \frac{\Delta u}{r}\, d\tau = \iint\limits_S \left( \frac{1}{r}\frac{\partial u}{\partial n} - u\frac{\partial \frac{1}{r}}{\partial n} \right) dS +$$

$$+ \iint\limits_{\sigma_\rho} \left( \frac{1}{r}\frac{\partial u}{\partial n} - u\frac{\partial \frac{1}{r}}{\partial n} \right) dS. \qquad (18.6)$$

If we now allow $\rho$ to tend to zero, the integral on the left of this formula will be evaluated throughout $D$. The surface integral over $S$ on the right-hand side of (18.6) is independent of $\rho$. We shall show that the second term on the right tends to the limit $-4\pi u(x_0, y_0, z_0)$. On the surface of $\sigma_\rho$, $r = \rho = $ const and since the normal $n$ is opposite in direction to the radius of the sphere, we have

$$\frac{\partial \frac{1}{r}}{\partial n}\bigg|_{\sigma_\rho} = -\frac{\partial \frac{1}{r}}{\partial r}\bigg|_{r=\rho} = \frac{1}{\rho^2}$$

and therefore

$$\iint\limits_{\sigma_\rho} u\,\frac{\partial \frac{1}{r}}{\partial n}\, dS = \frac{1}{\rho^2} \iint\limits_{\sigma_\rho} u\, dS = \frac{1}{\rho^2} u(M_\rho) 4\pi\rho^2 =$$

$$= 4\pi u(M_\rho) \to 4\pi u(M_0) \quad \text{when } \rho \to 0,$$

since $u(x, y, z)$ is continuous in $D$ and $M_\rho$ is a point on $\sigma_\rho$. The first-order derivatives of $u(x, y, z)$ are bounded in $\bar{D}$ since by hypothesis the function $u(x, y, z)$ has continuous first-order derivatives in the closed domain $\bar{D}$. Consequently, their exists a number $K$, such that $|\partial u/\partial n| < K$. We then have

$$\left| \iint\limits_{\sigma_\rho} \frac{1}{r} \frac{\partial u}{\partial n} \, dS \right| \leqslant \frac{K}{\rho} \iint\limits_{\sigma_\rho} dS =$$

$$= \frac{K}{\rho} 4\pi\rho^2 = 4\pi K\rho \to 0 \quad \text{when } \rho \to 0.$$

and on passing to the limit $\rho \to 0$ we obtain

$$\iiint\limits_{D} \frac{\Delta u}{r} \, d\tau = \iint\limits_{S} \frac{1}{r} \frac{\partial u}{\partial n} - u \frac{\partial \frac{1}{r}}{\partial n} \, dS - 4\pi u(x_0, y_0, z_0),$$

from which (18.5) follows directly.

In order to free our analysis from the assumption that the second-order derivatives of $u$ are continuous right up to $S$, let us replace the domain $D$ by $D^{(n)}$ which lies entirely inside $D$. We shall then apply (18.5) to $D^{(n)}$ and then by passing to the limit $D^{(n)} \to D$ we shall obtain the required result.

Completely analogous formulae are valid on a plane:

$$\iint\limits_{B} (u \Delta v - v \Delta u) \, d\sigma = \int\limits_{l} \left( u \frac{\partial v}{\partial n} - v \frac{\partial u}{\partial n} \right) dS, \tag{18.7}$$

$$u(x_0, y_0) = \frac{1}{2\pi} \int\limits_{l} \left( \ln \frac{1}{r} \frac{\partial u}{\partial n} - u \frac{\partial \ln \frac{1}{r}}{\partial n} \right) dS -$$

$$- \frac{1}{2\pi} \iint\limits_{B} \ln \frac{1}{r} \Delta u \, d\sigma, \tag{18.8}$$

where $B$ is a finite region bounded by the closed curve $l$ and $n$ is the outward normal to the curve $l$.

## § 19. Basic properties and harmonic functions

Let $u(x, y, z)$ by a harmonic function in a finite domain $D$ bounded by a surface $S$. We shall suppose that $u$ and its second-order derivatives are continuous right up to the surface $S$. If we let $v = u$ in Green's formula (18.2) and recall that $u$ is a harmonic function, we obtain

$$\int\int_S u \frac{\partial u}{\partial n} dS = \int\int\int_D \left[ \left(\frac{\partial u}{\partial x}\right)^2 + \left(\frac{\partial u}{\partial y}\right)^2 + \left(\frac{\partial u}{\partial z}\right)^2 \right] d\tau.$$

Since the volume integral is nonnegative, it follows that

$$\int\int_S u \frac{\partial u}{\partial n} dS \geqslant 0. \tag{19.1}$$

If we apply Green's formula (18.4) to the harmonic functions $u(x, y, z)$ and $v(x, y, z) = 1$, we obtain

$$\int\int_S \frac{\partial u}{\partial n} dS = 0, \tag{19.2}$$

i.e., the integral of the normal derivative of a harmonic function over the boundary of the domain is equal to zero. If we now apply equation (18.5) to the harmonic function $u(x, y, z)$, we obtain

$$u(x_0, y_0, z_0) = \frac{1}{4\pi} \int\int_S \left( \frac{1}{r} \frac{\partial u}{\partial n} - u \frac{\partial \frac{1}{r}}{\partial n} \right) dS, \tag{19.3}$$

since $\Delta u = 0$, i.e. the value of a harmonic function at any point inside a finite domain can be expressed in terms of its values and the values of its normal derivative on the surface of the domain.

*Remarks.* The integrals in (19.1), (19.2) and (19.3) do not contain second-order derivatives of $u(x, y, z)$ and in order to ensure that they are valid it is sufficient to assume that the harmonic function and its first-order derivatives are continuous right up to $S$. In order to establish this, it is sufficient to replace $D$ by $D^{(n)}$ lying wholly inside $D$ and to write down (19.1), (19.2) and (19.3) for $D^{(n)}$ in which the second-order derivatives are also continuous right up to the surface $S^{(n)}$ and then pass to the limit $D^{(n)} \to D$.

*The function $u(x, y, z)$ which is harmonic in the domain $D$ has derivatives of all orders inside this domain.* In fact, consider an arbitrary point $(x_0, y_0, z_0)$ in $D$, and surround it by a surface $S'$ which lies wholly inside $D$. Since $u(x, y, z)$ is harmonic in $D$, it is also harmonic in the domain bounded by $S'$ and has continuous second-order derivatives right up to $S'$. Using (19.3) we have

$$u(x_0, y_0, z_0) = \frac{1}{4\pi} \iint_{S'} \left( \frac{1}{r} \frac{\partial u}{\partial n} - u \frac{\partial \frac{1}{r}}{\partial n} \right) dS. \tag{19.3'}$$

Since the point $(x_0, y_0, z_0)$ does not lie on $S'$, it follows that

$$\frac{1}{r} = \frac{1}{\sqrt{(x - x_0)^2 + (y - y_0)^2 + (z - z_0)^2}}$$

is continuous and has continuous derivatives of any order with respect to $x_0, y_0, z_0$. Consequently, the right-hand side of (19.3') can be differentiated under the integral sign any number of times with respect to $x_0, y_0, z_0$. This proves the above statement.

*Theorem 1. The value of a harmonic function at the center of a sphere is equal to the arithmetic mean of its values on the surface of this sphere.* Let $u(x, y, z)$ be a harmonic function inside the sphere. We shall suppose that this function and its first derivatives are continuous right up to the surface of the sphere and denote the center of the sphere by $M_0(x_0, y_0, z_0)$, its radius by $R$ and its surface by $S_R$. Using (19.3) we obtain

$$u(x_0, y_0, z_0) = \frac{1}{4\pi} \iint_{S_R} \left( \frac{1}{r} \frac{\partial u}{\partial n} - u \frac{\partial \frac{1}{r}}{\partial n} \right) dS. \tag{19.4}$$

On $S_R$ the radial distance $r$ remains constant and equal to $R$. Since the direction of the outward normal to $S_R$ is the same as the direction of the radius vector, we have

$$\frac{\partial}{\partial n}\left(\frac{1}{r}\right)\Bigg|_{r=R} = \frac{\partial \frac{1}{r}}{\partial r}\Bigg|_{r=R} = -\frac{1}{R^2},$$

and (18.12) yields

$$u(x_0, y_0, z_0) = \frac{1}{4\pi R} \iint\limits_{S_R} \frac{\partial u}{\partial n}\, dS + \frac{1}{4\pi R^2} \iint\limits_{S_R} u\, dS$$

or, in view of (19.2), we have finally

$$u(x_0, y_0, z_0) = \frac{1}{4\pi R^2} \iint\limits_{S} u\, dS =$$

$$= \frac{1}{4\pi} \int\limits_0^\pi \int\limits_0^{2\pi} u(R, \theta, \varphi) \sin \theta\, d\theta\, d\varphi. \tag{19.5}$$

*Theorem 2. A function which is harmonic inside a bounded domain D and continuous in a closed domain $\bar{D}$ reaches its greatest and smallest values only on the boundary of the region, except when the function is equal to a constant.*

*Proof.* Suppose $u(M)$ reaches its greatest value at an internal point $M_0(x, y, z)$ of $D$. If we draw a sphere $S_\rho$ centered on $M_0$ and having radius $\rho$ which lies wholly inside $D$, and apply theorem 1 to it, and then replace the integrand $u(M)$ by its greatest value $u_\rho^{(\max)}$ on the sphere $S_\rho$, we obtain

$$u(M_0) = \frac{1}{4\pi\rho^2} \iint\limits_{S_\rho} u\, dS \leqslant \frac{1}{4\pi\rho^2} \iint\limits_{S_\rho} u_\rho^{(\max)} dS = u_\rho^{(\max)},$$

where the equality sign is to be used only when $u = u(M_0) = $ const on $S_\rho$. Since by hypothesis $u(M_0)$ is the greatest value of $u(M)$ in $D$, we may conclude that we must use the equality sign, and consequently $u(M)$ is constant both inside and on the surface of any sphere centered on $M_0$ and lying wholly inside $D$. We shall show that as a consequence of this $u(M)$ is also constant throughout $D$. Let $N$ be any internal point of $D$. It is required to show that

$u(N) = u(M_0)$. Let us join $M_0$ and $N$ by a line $l$ of finite length, for example a broken line lying inside $D$, and let $d$ be the shortest distance $l$ from the boundary of $S$ of $D$. In view of the above, $u(M)$ is equal to the constant $u(M_0)$ in a sphere centred on $M_0$ and having radius of $\frac{1}{2}d$. Suppose $M_1$ is the last point of intersection of the line $l$ with the surface of this sphere if we count from $M_0$. We have $u(M_1) = u(M_0)$, and in view of the above discussion $u(M)$ is also equal to the constant $u(M_0)$ in the sphere centered on $M_1$ and the radius $\frac{1}{2}d$. Suppose that $M_2$ is the last point of intersection of $l$ with the surface of this sphere. As before, the function $u(M)$ is also equal to the constant $u(M_0)$ in the sphere centred on $M_2$ with radius $\frac{1}{2}d$, and so on. By constructing a finite number of such spheres the entire line $l$ can be covered by spheres. The point $N$ will then be found to lie inside one of these spheres and therefore $u(N) = u(M_0)$. Similarly, it can be shown that a harmonic function cannot reach its smallest value inside $D$. In accordance with Weierstrass's theorem, the function $u(M)$ reaches its greatest and smallest values in a closed bounded domain and, in particular, reaches them on the boundary of $D$ since it has been shown above that inside $D$ the harmonic function $u(M)$ cannot reach its greatest and smallest values. This proves the theorem.
It is quite easy to show that the harmonic function $u(M)$ cannot have either maxima or minima inside $D$.

## § 20. Formulation of basic problems for the Laplace equation

Let $S$ be a closed surface and let $D_i$ represent finite domains bounded by this surface while $D_e$ is an infinite domain external to $D_i$ also bounded by $S$. Suppose that the continuous functions $f_1(P)$, $f_2(P)$ and $f_3(P)$ are specified on $S$.

1. Internal Dirichlet problem. It is required to find a function $u(M)$ which is harmonic in the domain $D_i$, continuous in a closed domain $\bar{D}_i$ and which assumes on the surface $S$ the value

$$u|_S = f_1(P). \tag{20.1}$$

Similarly, the external Dirichlet problem involves determination of a function which is harmonic in $D_e$, continuous in $\bar{D}_e$ and satisfying the condition given by (20.1).

2. Internal Neumann problem. It is required to find the function $u(M)$ which is harmonic in a domain $D_i$ such that its derivative $\partial u/\partial n$ along the outward normal at each point on the surface $S$ is equal to the value of the given function $f_2(P)$ at the same point, i.e.

$$\left.\frac{\partial u}{\partial n}\right|_S = f_2(P). \tag{20.2}$$

Similarly, the external Neumann problem involves determination of a function $u(M)$ which is the harmonic in $D_e$ and whose normal derivative on $S$ satisfies the condition given by (20.2).

3. Third boundary value problem. It is required to find a function $u(M)$ which is harmonic in $D_i$, continuous in $\bar{D}_i$ and such that $\partial u/\partial n + a(P)u$ is equal at each point on $S$ to the value at this point of the given function $f_3(P)$, i.e.

$$\left.\frac{\partial u}{\partial n} + a(P)u\right|_S = f_3(P),$$

where $a(P) > 0$ is a given continuous function on $S$.

The third external boundary value problem can be formulated in a similar way.

*Theorem 3. The solutions of the internal and external Dirichlet problems are unique.*

*Proof.* To begin with, consider the internal Dirichlet problem. We shall suppose that there exist two solutions $u_1(M)$ and $u_2(M)$ of a given Dirichlet problem. Their differences $u(M) = u_1(M) - u_2(M)$ will be a harmonic function equal to zero on $A$. Hence, in view of theorem 2, it follows that $u(M) \equiv 0$, i.e. $u_1(M) = u_2(M)$ throughout $D$ since otherwise it would have to reach its greatest maximum value or its smallest negative value within $D$, which is impossible. Consider now the external Dirichlet problem. As before, let us suppose that there are two solutions $u_1(M)$ and $u_2(M)$. Their difference $u(M) = u_1(M) - u_2(M)$ will be a harmonic function equal to zero on $S$ and $u(M) \to 0$ as $M \to \infty$, i.e. for any $\varepsilon > 0$ we can find $R$ such that $|u(M)| < \varepsilon$ if $r \leqslant R$, where $r$ is the distance of $M$ from the origin. Suppose that $P(x, y, z)$ is an arbitrary point of the infinite domain $D_e$. Let us draw a sphere $S_r$ centred on the origin and having radius $r \geqslant R$, which is large enough for $P$ and $S$ to lie inside this sphere. We then have $|u(P)| < \varepsilon$, which follows from the extremal theorem, as applied to the finite domain $D_1$, lying between $S$ and $S_r$. Since $\varepsilon > 0$ is arbitrary, we conclude that $u(P) = 0$ and since $P$ is an arbitrary point in $D$, it follows that $u \equiv 0$ in $D$, i.e. $u_1 = u_2$.

## § 21. Green's function for the Laplace operator

**1. Green's function for the Dirichlet problem.** Let $u(M)$ be a harmonic function inside a finite domain $D$. Moreover, suppose that $u(M)$ and its first derivatives are continuous right up to the boundary $S$ of the domain $D$. It was shown in § 19 that under these conditions

$$u(M_0) = \frac{1}{4\pi} \int \int_S \left( \frac{1}{r} \frac{\partial u}{\partial n} - u \frac{\partial \frac{1}{r}}{\partial n} \right) dS, \tag{21.1}$$

where $r$ is the distance between the point $M_0$ inside $D$ and the running point $m$ on the surface $S$.

Suppose further that we have a given function $g(M, M_0)$ which has the following two properties: (1) as a function of the variable point $M$ it is harmonic inside $D$ and has continuous first derivatives right up to the surface $S$; (2) on $S$ the function $g(M, M_0)$ assumes the value $-1/4\pi r$. If we apply Green's formula (18.4) to the harmonic functions $u(M)$ and $g(M, M_0)$, we obtain

$$\int \int_S \left[ u(M) \frac{\partial g(M, M_0)}{\partial n} - g(M, M_0) \frac{\partial u(M)}{\partial n} \right] dS = 0$$

or, in view of the boundary values of the function $g(M, M_0)$,

$$\int \int_S \left[ u(M) \frac{\partial g(M, M_0)}{\partial n} + \frac{1}{4\pi r} \frac{\partial u(M)}{\partial n} \right] dS = 0.$$

On subtracting this equation from (21.1) we find that

$$u(M_0) = - \int \int_S u(M) \frac{\partial}{\partial n} \left[ \frac{1}{4\pi r} + g(M, M_0) \right] dS. \tag{21.2}$$

Let

$$G(M, M_0) = \frac{1}{4\pi r} + g(M, M_0).$$

This function is called *Green's function of the Dirichlet problem* for the Laplace equation.

*Definition. Green's function of the Dirichlet problem for the Laplace equation is defined as the function $G(M, M_0)$ which satisfies the following conditions*: (1) $G(M, M_0)$ *regarded as a function of the point $M$ is harmonic inside the domain $D$ except for the point $M_0$, where it becomes infinite*; (2) *it satisfies the boundary condition*

$$G(M, M_0)_S = 0; \tag{21.3}$$

*and* (3) *in the domain $D$ the function $G(M, M_0)$ is given by*

$$G(M, M_0) = \frac{1}{4\pi r} + g(M, M_0), \tag{21.4}$$

*where $r = |M_0, M|$ and $g(M, M_0)$ is a harmonic function throughout $D$.*

The determination of Green's function can be reduced to the determination of its regular part $g(M, M_0)$, which is found by solving the Dirichlet problem:

$$\Delta g(M, M_0) = 0, \quad g(M, M_0)|_S = -\frac{1}{4\pi r} \qquad (M_0 \in D). \tag{21.5}$$

The solution of the internal Dirichlet problem (if it exists) can be expressed in terms of Green's function:

$$u(M_0) = -\int\int_S f(M) \frac{\partial G(M, M_0)}{\partial n} dS, \quad u(M)|_S = f(M). \tag{21.6}$$

In deriving this formula, we assume the existence of the function $u(M)$, i.e. the solution of the internal Dirichlet problem with boundary values $f(M)$ which is continuous together with its first derivatives right up to the boundary $S$. The required function in the Dirichlet problem should, on the other hand, be harmonic inside $D$ and continuous in a closed domain $\bar{D}$. Therefore, although we have not proved the existence of the solution, equation (21.6) is in fact the integral representation of existing sufficiently smooth solutions of the Dirichlet problem. Detailed studies of (21.6) which were carried out by A. M. Lyapunov showed that for surfaces now known as Lyapunov surfaces (see § 30), this expression gives the solution of the Dirichlet problem for any continuous $f(M)$.

Green's function for the external Dirichlet problem can be introduced in an analogous way.

**2. Some properties of Green's function.** (a) *Green's function* $G(M, M_0)$ *is positive throughout the domain* $D$. In point of fact, $G(M, M_0)$ vanishes on $S$ and is positive on the surface of a small enough sphere centred on $M_0$ (since $G(M, M_0) \to +\infty$ as $M \to M_0$). Hence, in view of theorem 2 (§ 19) it follows that the function is positive throughout the domain $D$.

We shall derive one further simple inequality for $G(M, M_0)$. The function $g(M, M_0)$ assumes a negative boundary value $-1/4\pi r$ on $S$ and hence $g(M, M_0) < 0$ in the closed domain $\bar{D}$ so that

$$0 < G(M, M_0) < \frac{1}{4\pi r} \quad \text{(within } D\text{).} \tag{21.7}$$

(b) *Green's function is symmetric*, i.e.

$$G(M, M_0) = G(M_0, M). \tag{21.8}$$

To prove this, let us apply Green's formula (18.4) to the functions $u = G(M, M_1)$ and $v = G(M, M_2)$. The region of integration $D_2$ can be chosen to be the region obtained from $D$ by excluding two spheres centred on $M_1$ and $M_2$ with small radii $\varepsilon$. The triple integral over this region will vanish, since both $u$ and $v$ are harmonic at all points other than $M_1$ and $M_2$. The integral over $S$ is also zero, in view of the boundary condition given by (21.3). We thus arrive at the equation

$$\iint\limits_{S_1} \left[ G(M, M_1) \frac{\partial G(M, M_2)}{\partial n} - G(M, M_2) \frac{\partial G(M, M_1)}{\partial n} \right] dS +$$

$$+ \iint\limits_{S_2} \left[ G(M, M_1) \frac{\partial G(M, M_2)}{\partial n} - \right.$$

$$\left. - G(M, M_2) \frac{\partial G(M, M_1)}{\partial n} \right] dS = 0,$$

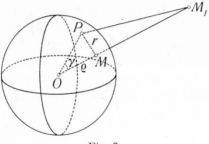

Fig. 9.

where $S_1$ and $S_2$ are the surfaces of the two spheres mentioned above. As $\varepsilon \to 0$, the integral over $S_1$ which is centred on $M_1$ will clearly tend to $G(M_1, M_2)$, whilst the integral over $S_2$ which is centred on $M_2$ will tend to $G(M_2, M_1)$, which in fact proves the symmetry of Green's function.

*Remark.* In the case of a plane, the Green's function becomes

$$G(M, M_0) = \frac{1}{2\pi} \ln \frac{1}{r} + g(M, M_0), \quad r = |M_0M|.$$

The solution of the internal Dirichlet problem is expressed by (21.6) except that $S$ now represents a curve bounding the plane domain $B$.

## § 22. Solution of the internal Dirichlet problem for a sphere

Suppose it is required to find the function $u(M)$ which is harmonic inside a sphere, continuous in a closed sphere, and assumes given continuous values $f(P)$ on the surface $S$ of the sphere. To begin with, let us consider Green's function in the sphere. Let $R$ be the radius of the sphere which is centred on the point $O$ and consider an arbitrary point $M(x, y, z)$. Moreover, let $\rho$ be the distance of this point from the centre of the sphere (fig. 9). If we subject the point $M$ to the inversion transformation with respect to the sphere $S$, we obtain a point $M_1(x_1, y_1, z_1)$ which lies on the straight line $OM$ at a distance $\rho_1$ from the centre of the sphere, where

$$\rho\rho_1 = R^2. \tag{22.1}$$

Let us now take an arbitrary point $P(\xi, \eta, \zeta)$ and let $r$ and $r_1$ be the distances of this point from $M$ and $M_1$. We shall find the relationship between $r$ and $r_1$ when the point $P$ lies on the surface of the sphere. The triangles $OMP$ and $OM_1P$ are similar, since they have a common angle at $O$ and the sides forming this angle are proportional in view of (22.1). It follows that

$$\frac{r}{r_1} = \frac{\rho}{R}$$

or

$$\frac{1}{r} - \frac{R}{\rho}\frac{1}{r_1} = 0 \quad \text{(point $P$ on $S$)}. \tag{22.2}$$

This is the required relationship between $r$ and $r_1$.

We shall now show that the Green's function for the sphere is

$$G(P, M) = \frac{1}{4\pi r} - \frac{1}{4\pi}\frac{R}{\rho}\frac{1}{r_1}. \tag{22.3}$$

In fact, the function $G(P, M)$, when regarded as a function of the point $P$, is harmonic inside the sphere with the exception of the point $M$, where it becomes infinite. It vanishes on the surface $S$ of the sphere, which follows from (22.2). Therefore, the above function satisfies all the conditions imposed on the Green's function of the Dirichlet problem. Substituting the above Green's function into (21.6) we obtain

$$u(M) = -\frac{1}{4\pi} \int\int_S f(P) \frac{\partial\left(\dfrac{1}{r} - \dfrac{R}{\rho}\dfrac{1}{r_1}\right)}{\partial n} dS. \tag{22.4}$$

We can transform this formula as follows:

$$\frac{\partial}{\partial n}\left(\frac{1}{r}\right) = \frac{\partial \frac{1}{r}}{\partial \xi}\cos(n\xi) + \frac{\partial \frac{1}{r}}{\partial \eta}\cos(n\eta) + \frac{\partial \frac{1}{r}}{\partial \zeta}\cos(n\zeta) =$$

$$= -\frac{1}{r^2}\left[\frac{\xi - x}{r}\cos(n\xi) + \frac{\eta - y}{r}\cos(n\eta) + \right.$$

$$+ \frac{\zeta - z}{r} \cos (n\zeta) \Big] = - \frac{1}{r^2} [\cos (r\xi) \cos (n\xi) +$$

$$+ \cos (r\eta) \cos (n\eta) + \cos (r\zeta) \cos (n\zeta)] = - \frac{1}{r^2} \cos (r, n).$$

Similarly,

$$\frac{\partial}{\partial n} \left( \frac{1}{r_1} \right) = - \frac{1}{r_1^2} \cos (r_1, n).$$

so that

$$\frac{\partial \left( \dfrac{1}{r} - \dfrac{R}{\rho} \dfrac{1}{r_1} \right)}{\partial n} = - \frac{1}{r^2} \cos (r, n) + \frac{R}{\rho} \frac{\cos (r_1, n)}{r_1^2} \quad \text{(on } S\text{)}.$$

$$(22.5)$$

From the triangles $OMP$ and $OM_1P$ we have

$$\rho^2 = R^2 + r^2 - 2Rr \cos (r, n),$$

$$\rho_1^2 = R^2 + r_1^2 - 2Rr_1 \cos (r_1, n) \quad \text{(point } P \text{ on } S\text{)}.$$

Substituting for $\cos (r, n)$ and $\cos (r_1, n)$ from these two expressions into (22.5) we have

$$\frac{\partial \left( \dfrac{1}{r} - \dfrac{R}{\rho} \dfrac{1}{r_1} \right)}{\partial n} = \frac{\rho^2 - R^2 - r^2}{2Rr^3} + \frac{R^2 + r_1^2 - \rho_1^2}{2\rho r_1^3}$$

or, in view of (22.1) and (22.2),

$$\frac{\partial}{\partial n} \left( \frac{1}{r} - \frac{R}{\rho} \frac{1}{r_1} \right) = \frac{\rho^2 - R^2}{Rr^3} \quad \text{(on } S\text{)}.$$

If we now substitute this into (22.4), we finally have

$$u(M) = \frac{1}{4\pi R} \int \int_S f(P) \frac{R^2 - \rho^2}{r^3} \, dS. \qquad (22.6)$$

which is known as *Poisson's formula*.

We thus see that if the solution of the internal Dirichlet problem for a sphere exists, and is continuous in a closed sphere together with its first derivatives, then this solution is given by the Poisson formula (22.6).

We shall show that if $f(P)$ is continuous, then (22.6) gives the solution of the internal Dirichlet problem for a sphere. To prove this, we must show that the integral in (22.6) is a harmonic function inside the sphere and that $u(M)$ as given by (22.6) is continuous in a closed sphere and assumes the given continuous values $f(P)$ on the surface of the sphere, i.e. as point $M$ approaches an arbitrary point $P$ on the surface of the sphere, $u(M)$ tends to the value $f$ at this point. At the same time, $u(M)$ becomes continuous in the closed sphere if it is suitably defined on the surface of the sphere.

The harmonic property of the function $u(M)$ follows from the fact that when $\rho < R$

$$\Delta \frac{R^2 - \rho^2}{r^3} = \Delta \frac{R^2 + r^2 - \rho^2}{r^3} - \Delta \frac{1}{r} =$$

$$= -2R\Delta \frac{\partial \frac{1}{r}}{\partial n} = -2R \frac{\partial}{\partial n} \Delta \frac{1}{r} = 0 \quad (P \text{ on } S).$$

Let us take an arbitrary point $N$ on the surface of the sphere and show that $u(M) \to f(N)$ as $M \to N$. We note that (22.6) is valid in the special case when $f(P) \equiv 1$ when the solution of the Dirichlet problem clearly exists. (It is identically equal to 1). Therefore, we have

$$1 = \frac{1}{4\pi R} \iint\limits_{S} \frac{R^2 - \rho^2}{r^3} \, dS. \tag{22.7}$$

If we multiply both sides of this expression by $f(N)$, and then subtract it from Poisson's equation (22.6), we obtain

$$u(M) - f(N) = \frac{1}{4\pi R} \iint\limits_{S} [f(P) - f(N)] \frac{R^2 - \rho^2}{r^3} \, dS. \tag{22.8}$$

Let us now draw a sphere of small radius $2\delta$ centered on $N$ and choose $\delta$ to be so small that at all points on the surface $S$ which fall inside the sphere we have

$$|f(P) - f(N)| < \frac{\varepsilon}{2}, \tag{22.9}$$

where $\varepsilon > 0$ is an arbitrary given small number $f(P)$ being continuous.

Let $\sigma$ denote the part of $S$ which lies inside the sphere centred on $N$ and having radius $2\delta$, and let $S - \sigma$ denote the remainder. The difference given by (22.8) can then be written in the form

$$u(M) - f(N) = \frac{1}{4\pi R} \int\!\!\int_{\sigma} [f(P) - f(N)] \frac{R^2 - \rho^2}{r^3} dS +$$

$$+ \frac{1}{4\pi R} \int\!\!\int_{S-\sigma} [f(P) - f(N)] \frac{R^2 - \rho^2}{r^3} dS. \tag{22.10}$$

Let us consider each of the terms on the right of (22.10). In view of (22.9) and (22.7) we have

$$\left| \frac{1}{4\pi R} \int\!\!\int_{\sigma} [f(P) - f(N)] \frac{R^2 - \rho^2}{r^3} dS \right| <$$

$$< \frac{\varepsilon}{2} \frac{1}{4\pi R} \int\!\!\int_{\sigma} \frac{R^2 - \rho^2}{r^3} dS < \frac{\varepsilon}{2} \frac{1}{4\pi R} \int\!\!\int_{S} \frac{R^2 - \rho^2}{r^3} dS = \frac{\varepsilon}{2}. \tag{22.11}$$

This is valid whatever the position of $M$ inside the sphere.

To estimate the second integral in (22.10) let us draw a new sphere of radius $\delta$ and again centered on $N$. We shall suppose that as the point $M$ tends to $N$ the former lies inside the sphere. Under these conditions we have $r = |MP| > \delta$ if $P$ is on $S - \sigma$. The function $f(P)$ is continuous on the surface $S$ of the sphere and is therefore bounded, i.e. $|f(P)| \leqslant K$. We then have the following inequality for the second integral

$$\left| \frac{1}{4\pi R} \int\!\!\int_{S-\sigma} [f(P) - f(N)] \frac{R^2 - \rho^2}{r^3} dS \right| \leqslant \frac{2KR(R^2 - \rho^2)}{\delta^3}.$$

As $M \to N$ the difference $R^2 - \rho^2$ tends to zero, and consequently

$$\left| \frac{1}{4\pi R} \iint\limits_{S-\sigma} [f(P) - f(N)] \frac{R^2 - \rho^2}{r^3} \, dS \right| < \frac{\varepsilon}{2}. \tag{22.12}$$

In view of (22.11) and (22.12) we have from (22.10)

$$|u(M) - f(N)| < \varepsilon,$$

and hence, since $\varepsilon > 0$ is arbitrary, it follows that $\lim\limits_{M \to N} u(M) = f(N)$
which was to be proved.

*Remark* (1). Let us now introduce spherical coordinates with the origin at 0. Let $\theta'$, $\varphi'$ be the angular coordinates of the point $P$ and $\rho$, $\theta$, $\varphi$ the polar coordinates of $M$. If $\gamma$ denotes the angle between the vectors $\overline{OP}$ and $\overline{OM}$, Poisson's formula (22.6) may be written in the form

$$u(\rho, \theta, \varphi) =$$

$$= \frac{R}{4\pi} \int\limits_0^{2\pi} \int\limits_0^{\pi} f(\theta', \varphi') \frac{R^2 - \rho^2}{(R^2 - 2R\rho \cos \gamma + \rho^2)^{\frac{3}{2}}} \sin \theta' \, d\theta' \, d\varphi'. \tag{22.13}$$

*Remark* (2). The solution of the internal Dirichlet problem for a circle is given by the Poisson integral

$$u(r, \theta) = \frac{1}{2\pi} \int\limits_{-\pi}^{\pi} f(t) \frac{R^2 - r^2}{R^2 - 2rR \cos (t - \theta) + r^2} \, dt. \tag{22.14}$$

A consequence of Poisson's formula. Consider a function $u(M)$ which is harmonic and non-negative throughout $D$. Let us draw a sphere $S$ centered on a point $M_0$ which lies wholly inside $D$, and let $R$ be its radius. If $M$ is any other point inside the sphere $S$ (fig. 10), then it is readily seen that the kernel $R^2 - \rho^2/4\pi R r^3$ of Poisson's formula satisfies the following inequalities for $\rho < R$

$$\frac{1}{4\pi R} \frac{R - \rho}{(R + \rho)^2} \leqslant \frac{1}{4\pi R} \frac{R^2 - \rho^2}{r^3} \leqslant$$

$$\leqslant \frac{1}{4\pi R} \frac{R + \rho}{(R - \rho)^2} \qquad (\rho = |M_0 M|),$$

and it follows directly from (22.6) that

$$\frac{R(R-\rho)}{(R+\rho)^2}\ \frac{1}{4\pi R^2}\int\int_S u(P)\,dS \leqslant u(M) \leqslant$$

$$\leqslant \frac{R(R+\rho)}{R(-\rho)^2}\ \frac{1}{4\pi R^2}\int\int_S u(P)\,dS$$

or, using the mean value theorem

$$\frac{R(R-\rho)}{(R+\rho)^2}\,u(M_0) \leqslant u(M) \leqslant \frac{R(R+\rho)}{(R-\rho)^2}\,u(M_0). \qquad (22.15)$$

This estimate of the values of a positive harmonic function at an arbitrary point of a sphere from its value at the centre of the sphere is known as Harnack's inequality.

*Theorem 4. A function which is harmonic in all space is identically equal to zero.*

*Proof.* Suppose $u(M)$ is a function which is harmonic in all space. Let us draw a sphere $S$ of arbitrary radius and centred on the origin. The values of this function inside the sphere can then be expressed in terms of its values on its surface with the aid of Poisson's formula:

$$u(M) = \frac{1}{4\pi R}\int\int_S u(P)\,\frac{R^2-\rho^2}{r^3}\,dS. \qquad (22.16)$$

If we now take $R$ to be so large that $|u(P)| < \varepsilon$ on the surface $S$

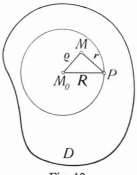

Fig. 10.

of the sphere, which is possible since $u(P) \to 0$ as $P \to \infty$, we have from (22.16)

$$|u(M)| \leqslant \frac{1}{4\pi R} \iint\limits_S |u(P)| \frac{R^2 - \rho^2}{r^3} \, dS \leqslant$$

$$\leqslant \varepsilon \frac{1}{4\pi R} \iint\limits_S \frac{R^2 - \rho^2}{r^3} \, dS$$

or, in view of (22.7), $|u(M)| < \varepsilon$. Since $\varepsilon > 0$ is arbitrary, it follows that $u(M) = 0$, and since $M$ is itself arbitrary $u \equiv 0$ in all space.

## § 23. Continuity theorems for harmonic functions

*Theorem 5. If a series of functions $u_n(M)$ $(n = 1, 2, 3, \ldots)$ which are harmonic in a bounded domain $D$ and continuous in $\overline{D}$ converges uniformly on the surface $S$ of the domain $D$, then it also converges uniformly inside $D$. The limiting function will be harmonic inside $D$.*
*Proof.* Since the series of functions is uniformly convergent on $S$, we can find any number $N > 0$ for any $\varepsilon > 0$ such that

$$|u_{n_1} - u_{n_2}| < \varepsilon \quad \text{(on } S\text{)}, \tag{23.1}$$

provided only $n_1 \geqslant N$, $n_2 \geqslant N$.
In view of the extremal theorem established above, the inequality given by (23.1) will also be valid inside $D$. Hence, from Cauchy's criterion we find that the series of harmonic functions $u_n(M)$ converges uniformly inside $D$ to the limiting function $u(M)$ which is continuous in the closed domain $\overline{D}$. We shall show that it is harmonic inside $D$. Let $M$ be an arbitrary point in $D$, and let us draw a sphere $S$ centered on $M$ and having a radius $R$ such that the entire sphere lies inside $D$. Since $u_n(M)$ are harmonic in $D$ each of them can be represented by the Poisson integral:

$$u_n(M) = \frac{1}{4\pi R} \iint\limits_S u_n(P) \frac{R^2 - \rho^2}{r^3} \, dS \quad (r = |PM|). \tag{23.2}$$

Since the series of functions $u_n(M)$ converges uniformly inside $D$

we can proceed to the limit in (23.2) and this yields

$$u(M) = \frac{1}{4\pi R} \iint\limits_{S} u(P) \frac{R^2 - \rho^2}{r^3} dS.$$

Hence it follows that $u(M)$ is harmonic inside the sphere $S$.

*Theorem 6. If an increasing series of functions $u_n(M)$ which are harmonic in a domain $D$ converges at an internal point $M_0$ of $D$, then it converges to a harmonic function $u(M)$ throughout the domain $D$ and the convergence is uniform in any closed domain $D_1$, which, together with its surface, lies inside $D$.*

*Proof.* By hypothesis, inside $D$ we have $u_{n+1}(M) \geqslant u_n(M)$. Since the series converges at $M_0$ for any given $\varepsilon > 0$, we can choose a number $N$ such that

$$0 \leqslant u_{n+P}(M_0) - u_n(M_0) \leqslant \varepsilon$$

for $n > N$ and any positive $p$. Let us draw a sphere $S$ of radius $R$ and centered on $M_0$, which lies wholly inside the domain $D$. Since $u_{n+P}(M) - u_n(M) \geqslant 0$ inside $D$, we have, using Harnack's inequality (22.15),

$$0 \leqslant u_{n+P}(M) - u_n(M) \leqslant \frac{R(R + \rho)}{(R - \rho)^2} \varepsilon,$$

where $M$ is an arbitrary point inside the sphere $S$ and $\rho$ is the distance between $M$ and $M_0$. If we now take a sphere $S'$ of radius $R - a$ and centred on $M_0$ where $a$ is a small positive number, we have in $S'$,

$$0 \leqslant u_{n+P}(M) - u_n(M) \leqslant \frac{2R^2}{a^2} \varepsilon,$$

From this it follows that the series $u_n(M)$ converges uniformly in $S'$. If we take some other point $M_1$ inside the sphere $S'$ and repeat the above analysis, taking into account the convergence of the series at $M_1$, we shall obtain the uniform convergence inside the sphere lying within $D$ and centered on this point. By continuing in this way we shall prove the uniform convergence of the series in any closed sphere lying within $D$. From Borel's lemma, any closed domain $D_1$ which, together with its surface, lies inside $D$, can be covered by a finite number of spheres lying inside $D$, and this leads us to the uniform convergence of $u_n(M)$ within $D_1$. In view of theorem 5, it follows from the uniform convergence of $u_n(M)$ that the limiting function $u(M)$ is harmonic inside $D$.

## § 24. The external Dirichlet problem for a sphere

Let $R$ be the radius of a sphere centered on the point $O$ and suppose we have a given continuous arbitrary function $f(P)$ on the surface $S$ of the sphere. The solution of the external Dirichlet problem for the sphere is given by the Poisson formula

$$u(M) = \frac{1}{4\pi R} \int\int_S f(P) \frac{\rho^2 - R^2}{r^3} \, dS, \qquad (24.1)$$

where $\rho = |OM|$, $r = |MP|$ and $\rho > R$.

As in § 23, we shall show that when $\rho > R$, i.e. outside the sphere, the function $u(M)$ given by the integral in (24.1) satisfies the Laplace equation (17.1). It remains to show that $u(M)$ tends uniformly to zero as $M \to \infty$. It is clear that $r > \rho - R$. If we take a point $M$ which is distant enough from the origin we have $\rho > 2R$, i.e. $R < \frac{1}{2}\rho$ so that $r > \frac{1}{2}\rho$. It follows that

$$\frac{1}{r^3} < \frac{8}{\rho^3} \quad \text{and} \quad \frac{\rho^2 - R^2}{r^3} < \frac{8(\rho^2 - R^2)}{\rho^3} < \frac{8}{\rho}$$

and consequently,

$$|u(M)| \leqslant \frac{1}{\rho} \frac{2}{\pi R} \int\int_S |f(P)| \, dS = \frac{C}{\rho},$$

where

$$C = \frac{2}{\pi R} \int\int_S |f(P)| \, dS.$$

Hence it is clear that as $\rho \to \infty$ the function $u(M)$ tends to zero. In order to verify that $u(M) \to f(N)$ as $M \to N$, we shall write the integral in (24.1) in terms of spherical polars:

$$u(\rho,\theta,\varphi) = \frac{R}{4\pi} \int\limits_{0}^{2\pi}\int\limits_{0}^{\pi} f(\theta'\,\varphi')\,\frac{\rho^2 - R^2}{(R^2 - 2R\rho\cos\gamma + \rho^2)^{\frac{3}{2}}}\sin\theta'\,d\theta'\,d\varphi',$$

(24.2)

where $(\rho, \theta, \varphi)$ are the polar coordinates of $M$ and $\theta'$, $\varphi'$ are the angular coordinates of the point $P$ and $\gamma = \angle\,MOP$. If we subject the point $M(\rho,\theta,\varphi)$ to the inversion transformation with respect to the sphere $S$ we obtain the transformed point $M_1(\rho_1, \theta, \varphi)$ which lies on the straight line $OM$ at a distance $\rho_1$ from the centre, where $\rho_1\rho = R^2$. The integral in (24.2) can also be written in the form

$$u(\rho,\theta,\varphi) = \frac{\rho_1}{4\pi} \int\limits_{0}^{2\pi}\int\limits_{0}^{\pi} f(\theta',\varphi')\,\frac{R^2 - \rho_1^2}{(R^2 - 2R\rho_1\cos\gamma + \rho_1^2)^{\frac{3}{2}}}\sin\theta'\,d\theta'\,d\varphi',$$

(24.3)

where $\rho_1 < R$ and when the point $M(\rho,\theta,\varphi)$ tends to an arbitrary point $N(R,\bar{\theta},\bar{\varphi})$ which lies on the sphere $S$, then the point $M_1(\rho_1,\theta,\varphi)$ would also tend to the point $N(R,\bar{\theta},\bar{\varphi})$.

In view of the result which we obtained for the internal Dirichlet problem for a sphere, we have

$$\frac{R}{4\pi} \int\limits_{0}^{2\pi}\int\limits_{0}^{\pi} f(\theta',\varphi')\,\frac{R^2 - \rho_1^2}{(R^2 - 2R\rho_1\cos\gamma + \rho_1^2)^{\frac{3}{2}}}\sin\theta'\,d\theta'\,d\varphi' \to f(N),$$

as $M_1 \to N$, and since $\rho_1 \to R$ (as $M \to N$), we conclude that the right hand side of (24.3) also tends to $f(N)$, which was to be proved.

## § 25. Behaviour of arbitrary harmonic functions at infinity

Let $u(M)$ be a harmonic function in an infinite domain $D_e$ which is external to $D_i$ which in turn is bounded by a closed surface $\Sigma$. We shall choose the origin to lie inside $D_i$ and draw a sphere $S$ centered on the origin and having a radius $R$ which is large enough for $\Sigma$ to lie wholly inside the sphere. The function $u(M)$ is harmonic in $D_e$, and therefore it must be harmonic outside $S$ and on the surface of the sphere. Consequently, outside $S$ the function $u(M)$ may be represented by the Poisson formula

$$u(M) = \frac{1}{4\pi R} \iint\limits_{S} u(P) \frac{\rho^2 - R^2}{r^3} dS \qquad (\rho > R), \qquad (25.1)$$

where

$$\rho = |OM| = \sqrt{x^2 + y^2 + z^2},$$

$$r = |MP| = \sqrt{(x - \xi)^2 + (y - \eta)^2 + (z - \zeta)^2}.$$

In § 24 we found that for large enough $\rho$

$$|u(M)| \leqslant \frac{C}{\rho}, \quad \text{where} \quad C = \frac{2}{\pi R} \iint\limits_{S} |u(P)| \, dS.$$

Differentiating (25.1) with respect to $x$ we obtain

$$\frac{\partial u}{\partial x} = \frac{1}{4\pi R} \iint\limits_{S} u(P) \frac{\partial}{\partial x} \left( \frac{\rho^2 - R^2}{r^3} \right) dS \quad (r \neq 0), \quad (25.2)$$

where

$$\frac{\partial}{\partial x} \left( \frac{\rho^2 - R^2}{r^3} \right) = \frac{2x}{r^3} - \frac{3(\rho^2 - R^2)}{r^4} \frac{x - \xi}{r}.$$

To estimate the derivative $\partial u/\partial x$, let us suppose that the point $M$ is far enough from the origin so that $\rho > 2R$, i.e. $R < \frac{1}{2}\rho$. We then have $r \geqslant \rho - R > \frac{1}{2}\rho$ and $\frac{1}{2} < 2/\rho$. We note that $|x| \leqslant \rho$, $|x - \xi|/r \leqslant 1$. In view of these inequalities we have

$$\left| \frac{\partial}{\partial x} \left( \frac{\rho^2 - R^2}{r^3} \right) \right| \leqslant \frac{64}{\rho^2},$$

and from (25.2) we have

$$\left| \frac{\partial u}{\partial x} \right| < \frac{1}{\rho^2} \frac{16}{\pi R} \iint\limits_{S} |u(P)| \, dS = \frac{A}{\rho^2},$$

where

$$A = \frac{16}{\pi R} \iint\limits_{S} |u(P)| \, dS.$$

Similarly,

$$\left|\frac{\partial u}{\partial y}\right| \leqslant \frac{A}{\rho^2}, \quad \left|\frac{\partial u}{\partial z}\right| < \frac{A}{\rho^2}.$$

It follows that in an infinite region $D'$ for points which are far enough from the origin, the harmonic function $u(M)$ satisfies the inequalities

$$|u(M)| < \frac{A}{\rho}, \quad \left|\frac{\partial u}{\partial x}\right| < \frac{A}{\rho^2}, \quad \left|\frac{\partial u}{\partial y}\right| < \frac{A}{\rho^2}, \quad \left|\frac{\partial u}{\partial z}\right| < \frac{A}{\rho^2},$$

(25.3)

where $A = $ const and $\rho$ is the distance of $M$ from the origin.

### § 26. Uniqueness theorem for the Neumann's problem

To begin with, let us consider the internal Neumann problem. Let $u_1(M)$ and $u_2(M)$ be two solutions of Neumann's problem for a domain $D$ bounded by $S$ which satisfies the same boundary condition

$$\frac{\partial u_1}{\partial n}\bigg|_S = f(N), \quad \frac{\partial u_2}{\partial n}\bigg|_S = f(N).$$

Their difference $u = u_1 - u_2$ will then be harmonic inside $D$ for which $\partial u/\partial n|_S = 0$.

Let us the first Green formula for harmonic functions

$$\int\int_S u \frac{\partial u}{\partial n} dS = \int\int\int_D \left[\left(\frac{\partial u}{\partial x}\right)^2 + \left(\frac{\partial u}{\partial y}\right)^2 + \left(\frac{\partial u}{\partial z}\right)^2\right] d\tau.$$

The left-hand side is zero, and therefore the right-hand side must also be zero. Since, however, $u(M)$ is continuous, and so are its first derivatives, it follows that

$$\frac{\partial u}{\partial x} = \frac{\partial u}{\partial y} = \frac{\partial u}{\partial z} = 0,$$

i.e. $u(M) = u_1(M) - u_2(M) = $ const, which was to be proved. We note that the internal Neumann problem is not always soluble.

The necessary condition for the solution to exist is

$$\iint\limits_{S} \frac{\partial u}{\partial n}\, dS = \iint\limits_{S} f(N)\, dS = 0.$$

This is a consequence of the properties of harmonic functions.
Let us consider now the external Neumann problem, and suppose that $u_1(M)$ and $u_2(M)$ are two solutions of this problem which satisfy the same boundary condition. Their difference is a harmonic function in an infinite domain for which

$$\left.\frac{\partial u}{\partial n}\right|_{S} = 0, \quad |u(M)| < \frac{A}{\rho}. \tag{26.1}$$

Let us take a sphere $S_R$ centered on the origin which has a large enough radius $R$ so that the surface $S$ lies wholly inside the sphere. Let $D_1$ be the domain bounded by $S$ and $S_R$. Using Green's formula for harmonic functions in the domain $D_1$ we obtain

$$\iint\limits_{S} u \frac{\partial u}{\partial n}\, dS + \iint\limits_{S_R} u \frac{\partial u}{\partial n}\, dS =$$

$$= \iiint\limits_{D_1} \left[ \left(\frac{\partial u}{\partial x}\right)^2 + \left(\frac{\partial u}{\partial y}\right)^2 + \left(\frac{\partial u}{\partial z}\right)^2 \right] d\tau$$

or, in view of (26.1)

$$\iiint\limits_{D_1} \left[ \left(\frac{\partial u}{\partial x}\right)^2 + \left(\frac{\partial u}{\partial y}\right)^2 + \left(\frac{\partial u}{\partial z}\right)^2 \right] d\tau = \iint\limits_{S_R} u \frac{\partial u}{\partial n}\, dS. \tag{26.2}$$

Since $u(M)$ is harmonic in the infinite domain, the inequalities given by (25.3) are valid. We have

$$\left| \frac{\partial u}{\partial n} \right| = \left| \frac{\partial u}{\partial x} \cos(nx) + \frac{\partial u}{\partial y} \cos(ny) + \right.$$

$$\left. + \frac{\partial u}{\partial z} \cos(nz) \right| \leqslant \frac{3A}{R^2} \quad \text{(on } S_R)$$

and

$$\left| \iint\limits_{S_R} u \frac{\partial u}{\partial n} \, dS \right| < \frac{3A}{R^3} \iint\limits_{S_R} dS = \frac{12\pi A}{R}.$$

For large enough $R$ we then have from (16.2)

$$\iiint\limits_{D_1} \left[ \left( \frac{\partial u}{\partial x} \right)^2 + \left( \frac{\partial u}{\partial y} \right)^2 + \left( \frac{\partial u}{\partial z} \right)^2 \right] d\tau < \varepsilon$$

for any $\varepsilon < 0$, which is only possible provided

$$\frac{\partial u}{\partial x} = \frac{\partial u}{\partial y} = \frac{\partial u}{\partial z} = 0.$$

It follows that $u = \text{const}$; since $u(M) \to 0$ as $M \to \infty$ we have $u(M) = 0$, i.e. $u_1(M) = u_2(M)$.

Chapter 6

## POTENTIAL THEORY

### § 27. Potentials due to volume distribution and to single and double layers

Consider an electric point charge $q$ placed at a point $A(a, b, c)$. The field at a point $M(x, y, z)$ other than $A$ is given by

$$E = kq \frac{r}{r^3}$$

or, in terms of components

$$E_x = kq \frac{x - a}{r^3}, \quad E_y = kq \frac{y - b}{r^3}, \quad E_z = kq \frac{z - c}{r^3}, \qquad (27.1)$$

where $r = \overline{AM}$, $r = |\overline{AM}|$ and $k$ is a proportionality coefficient whose value depends on the units employed. We shall assume for simplicity that $k = 1$.

It will be readily seen that the right-hand sides of the equations in (27.1) are equal to the partial derivatives with respect to $x$, $y$ and $z$ of the function

$$u(M) = \frac{q}{r} + \text{const} \qquad (27.2)$$

taken with a negative sign. This function is called the *electrostatic potential*. It is usual to set the arbitrary constant on the right of (27.2) equal to zero, so that $u(M) \to 0$ as $M$ tends to infinity. It follows that the potential due to a point charge $q$ is given by

$$u(M) = \frac{q}{r} = \frac{q}{\sqrt{(x - a)^2 + (y - b)^2 + (z - c)^2}}. \qquad (27.3)$$

If there is more than one charge, the resultant potential is equal to the sum of the individual potentials due to the individual point

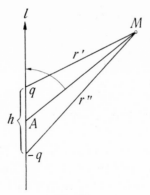

Fig. 11.

charges. In the case of a continuous distribution, the resultant potential is given by an appropriate integral.

Suppose that the charge is distributed throughout the domain $D$ with a volume density $\rho(N)$. The potential due to this distribution is then given by

$$v(M) = \iiint\limits_{D} \frac{\rho(N)}{r}\, d\tau \qquad (r = |\overline{MN}|). \qquad (27.4)$$

If the charge is distributed on the surface $S$ with a surface density $\rho(N)$, then the potential due to this distribution is

$$u(M) = \iint\limits_{S} \frac{\rho(N)}{r}\, dS, \qquad (27.5)$$

where $r$ is the distance between $M$ and the running point on the surface $S$.

Let us suppose now that we have two point charges $q$ and $-q$ which lie on a line $l$ and are at a distance $h$ from each other (fig. 11). If we let these two charges approach the point $A$ so that the direction of the line drawn from $-q$ to $q$ is the same as the positive direction of $l$, then the potential at any point other than $A$ will be equal to the difference of two equal quantities and will therefore be zero. If, on the other hand, $q$ is allowed to vary so that $qh = p = \text{const}$, the potential of the system will in the limit be given by

$$u(M) = \lim_{h \to 0} q \left( \frac{1}{r'} - \frac{1}{r''} \right) =$$

$$= \lim_{h \to 0} p \, \frac{\dfrac{1}{r'} - \dfrac{1}{r''}}{h} = p \, \frac{\partial \dfrac{1}{r}}{\partial l} = p \, \frac{\cos \overline{(AM, l)}}{r^2}. \tag{27.6}$$

In the limit, the system is referred to as a *dipole*, the quantity $p$ is the *dipole moment*, and $l$ the axis of the dipole. In practice, the dipole can only be realised approximately (two large charges separated by a small distance).

Suppose now that we have an oriented surface $S$, i.e. a surface for which the outer and inner sides are defined. If the surface $S$ carries a distribution of dipoles such that the dipole moment per unit area is $\mu(N)$, and all the dipoles are parallel to the direction of the outward normals, the potential due to the distribution is given by

$$w(M) = \int\!\!\int_S \mu(N) \, \frac{\cos (\overline{NM}, n_i)}{r^2} \, dS, \tag{27.7}$$

where the vector $r$ is drawn from $N$ to $M$ and $n_i$ is the new normal to $S$.

This integral is referred to as the *potential of a double layer*. Since the distribution of dipoles can be approximately realized by superimposing on the surface $S$ two distributions of charges, one with a density $\mu(N)/h$ and the other $-\mu(N)/h$ separated by a distance $h$ along the normal to $S$ where $h$ is small, we shall suppose that the vector $r$ has the direction of the line drawn from $M$ to $N$ and that the normal to $S$ is the outward normal. The potential of a double layer can then be written in the form

$$w(M) = - \int\!\!\int_S \mu(N) \, \frac{\partial \dfrac{1}{r}}{\partial n} \, dS = \int\!\!\int_S \mu(N) \, \frac{\cos \varphi}{r^2} \, dS, \tag{27.8}$$

where $\varphi$ is the angle between the outward normal $n$ and the vector $r$ drawn from $M$ to $N$.

## § 28. Improper integrals depending on a parameter

Improper integrals depending on a parameter are frequently encountered in potential theory. Let us therefore recall the main properties of such integrals.

1. Consider the integral

$$v(M) = \iiint\limits_{D} f(P, M) \, d\tau_P, \qquad (28.1)$$

where $f(P, M)$ is a continuous function in a finite domain $D$ except for a point $M$ in whose neighbourhood it increases without limit. If the function $f(P, M)$ satisfies the inequality

$$|f(P, M)| < \frac{C}{r^{\alpha}} \qquad (0 < \alpha < 3),$$

where $r$ is the distance between $P$ and $M$, then the improper integral (28.1) *converges absolutely*.

*Definition. The integral given by* (28.1) *is said to be uniformly convergent at a point $M_0$ if for any $\varepsilon > 0$ it is possible to find $\delta(\varepsilon)$ such that*

$$\left| \iiint\limits_{D_\delta} f(P, M) \, d\tau_P \right| < \varepsilon$$

*for any point $M$ whose distance from $M_0$ is less than $\delta(\varepsilon)$ and for any domain $D_\delta$ containing $M_0$ and having a diameter $d \leqslant \delta(\varepsilon)$.*

*Theorem. If the integral* (28.1) *is uniformly convergent at the point $M_0$ then it is a function of $M$ which is continuous at $M_0$.*

*Proof.* Let us take any $\varepsilon > 0$ and consider a domain $D_\delta$ containing $M_0$ in accordance with the definition of the uniform convergence of the integral (28.1) at the point. The integral (28.1) will be considered in two parts:

$$v(M) = \iiint\limits_{D_\delta} f(P, M) \, d\tau_P +$$

$$+ \iiint\limits_{D-D_\delta} f(P, M) \, d\tau_P = v_1(M) + v_2(M).$$

We then have

$$|v(M) - v(M_0)| \leqslant |v_1(M)| + |v_1(M_0)| + |v_2(M) - v_2(M_0)|.$$

Suppose that the point $M$ lies inside $D_\delta$, in which case, in view of the uniform convergence of (28.1), we have at $M_0$

$$|v_1(M)| \leqslant \frac{\varepsilon}{4}, \quad |v_1(M_0)| \leqslant \frac{\varepsilon}{4}$$

and consequently

$$|v(M) - v(M_0) < \frac{\varepsilon}{2} + |v_2(M) - v_2(M_0)|. \tag{28.2}$$

In the integral $v_2(M)$ the integration is carried out over the domain $D - D_\delta$, whilst the point $M_0$ lies inside $D_\delta$ and therefore the function $v_2(M)$ is continuous at $M_0$, and in its immediate vicinity. Therefore, for all $M$ close enough to $M_0$ we have

$$|v_2(M) - v_2(M_0)| < \frac{\varepsilon}{2}$$

and in view of (28.2)

$$|v(M) - v(M_0)| < \varepsilon,$$

Hence it follows that since $\varepsilon$ is arbitrary, the integral (28.1) is continuous at $M_0$, which was to be proved.

2. Suppose $S$ is a closed surface and let the function $F(P, M)$ be continuous when $P$ lies on $S$, whilst $M$ varies in space arbitrarily without becoming identical with $P$, and becomes infinite when $M$ and $P$ coincide. The integral

$$u(M) = \iint_S F(P, M) \, dS_P \tag{28.3}$$

is then a continuous function of the point $M$ when $M$ does not lie on $S$.

If the point $M$ coincides with some point $P_0$ on $S$, then $F(P, P_0)$ is a continuous function of $P$ on $S$ with the exception of the point $P_0$ in whose neighbourhood $F(P, P_0)$ increases without limit.

Let us exclude $P_0$ by surrounding it by a surface $\sigma_n$ having a diameter $\rho_n$. In the remaining region $S - \sigma_n$ the function $F(P, P_0)$ is continuous and bounded, and therefore the integral

$$\iint_{S-\sigma_n} F(P, P_0) \, dS_P. \tag{28.4}$$

exists.

If, when $\sigma_n$ shrinks on $P_0$, the integral (28.4) tends to a definite finite limit which is independent of the choice of $\sigma_n$, then this limit is called an *improper integral* of the function $F(P, P_0)$ over the surface $S$:

$$\iint\limits_{S} F(P, P_0)\, dS_P = \lim_{\rho_n \to 0}\ \iint\limits_{S-\sigma_n} F(P, P_0)\, dS_P. \qquad (28.5)$$

The integral given by (28.5) is said to be *absolutely convergent* if the integral

$$\iint\limits_{S} |F(P, P_0)|\, dS_P. \qquad (28.6)$$

converges. We note that the value of an absolutely convergent integral is independent of the way in which $\sigma_n$ shrinks on $P_0$.

If the integral (28.6) converges, then the integral (28.5) will also converge.

*Definition.* The integral given by (28.3) is said to be *uniformly convergent at the point* $P_0 \in S$ if for any $\varepsilon > 0$ one can find a neighbourhood $V(\varepsilon)$ of the point $P_0$ and a part $\sigma(\varepsilon)$ of $S$ containing $P_0$ within it such that for any point $M \in V(\varepsilon)$ the integral

$$\iint\limits_{S} F(P, M)\, dS_P$$

is less than $\varepsilon$ in absolute magnitude.

*Theorem. If the integral given by (28.3) converges uniformly at $P_0 \in S$, then as a function of $M$ it is continuous at $P_0$.*

The proof is very similar to that of the preceding theorem.

## § 29. Potential due to volume distribution

Consider the volume integral

$$v(M) = \int \int\limits_{D} \int \frac{\rho(N)}{r}\, d\tau \qquad (r = |MN|), \qquad (29.1)$$

where $D$ is a finite domain. Let us suppose that the density $\rho(N)$ is bounded and integrable in $D$. The integral in (29.1) is a proper integral if $M$ lies outside $D$ $(r \neq 0)$. In that case, the function $v(M)$ is continuous and possesses derivatives of all orders. These derivatives may be obtained by differentiation under the integral sign and $v(M)$ satisfies the Laplace equation $\Delta v = 0$ outside $D$. We shall show that as $M$ tends to infinity in any direction, the function $v(M)$ tends to zero so that

$$|v(M)| < \frac{A}{R}, \quad A = \text{const},$$

where $R$ is the distance between $M$ and the origin.

Let us suppose that the origin lies inside the domain $D$, in which case $MN \geqslant OM - ON$ or $r \geqslant R - ON$. Let $d$ be the diameter of the domain $D$ so that $r \geqslant R - d$. We shall suppose that the point $M$ is at a large distance from the origin so that $R > 2d$, i.e. $d < \frac{1}{2}R$ so that $r > \frac{1}{2}R$ or $1/r < 2/R$. We thus have

$$|v(M)| \leqslant \int\int\int_D |\rho(N)| \frac{d\tau}{r} < \frac{2}{R} \int\int\int_D |\rho(N)| \, d\tau = \frac{A}{R},$$

where

$$A = 2\iiint_D |\rho(N)| \, d\tau.$$

It follows that the potential $v(N)$ due to the volume distribution is a harmonic function outside the domain $D$.

Let us suppose now that $M$ lies inside $D$. The integral (29.1) is then improper, but since the density $\rho(N)$ is bounded, the integral converges since

$$\frac{|\rho(N)|}{r} < \frac{C}{r}.$$

*Theorem 1. If $\rho(N)$ is bounded and integrable in $D$, then the potential $v(M)$ and its first order partial derivatives are continuous in all space, and the derivatives can be obtained by differentiation under the integral sign.*

*Proof.* To begin with, we shall show that the integral (29.1) and also the integrals

$$X(M) = -\int\int\int_D \rho(N) \frac{x - \xi}{r^3} \, d\tau, \quad Y(M), \quad Z(M), \qquad (29.2)$$

which are obtained by differentiating (29.1) with respect to $x$, $y$

and $z$ under the integral sign respectively, converge uniformly at any point $M_0$. Suppose that $M_0$ is any point inside $D$, and consider a region $D_\delta$ which contains $M_0$ and lies wholly inside $D$. We shall calculate the modulus of the integral

$$\left| \iiint\limits_{D_\delta} \frac{\rho(N)}{r}\, d\tau \right| < C \iiint\limits_{K_\delta} \frac{d\tau}{r} \qquad (r = |MN|),$$

where $K_\delta$ is a sphere of radius $\delta$ centered on $M_0$ and containing $D_\delta$. In order to evaluate the latter integral, we shall use spherical polar coordinates with the origin at $M$. It is evident that

$$C \iiint\limits_{K_\delta} \frac{d\tau}{r} < C \iiint\limits_{K_{2\delta}} \frac{d\tau}{r} = C \int_0^{2\delta}\int_0^{\pi}\int_0^{2\pi} r \sin\, dr\, d\theta\, d\varphi = C \cdot 8\pi\delta^2,$$

where $K_{2\delta}$ is a sphere of radius $2\delta$ centred on $M$. Thus,

$$\left| \iiint\limits_{D_\delta} \frac{\rho(N)}{r}\, d\tau \right| < 8\pi C \delta^2 \to 0 \text{ when } \delta \to 0$$

independently of $M_0$, i.e. if we have a given $\varepsilon > 0$, then by choosing $\delta$ so that $\delta = \sqrt{\varepsilon/8\pi C}$ (independently of the choice of $M_0$), we can ensure the uniform convergence of (29.1) at any point $M_0$ in $D$. If we repeat this discussion for $X(N)$, we obtain

$$\left| \iiint\limits_{D_\delta} \rho(N) \frac{x-\xi}{r^3}\, d\tau \right| < C \iiint\limits_{K_\delta} \frac{d\tau}{r^2} <$$

$$< C \iiint\limits_{K_{2\delta}} \frac{d\tau}{r^2} = 8\pi C \delta < \varepsilon,$$

if $\delta < \delta(\varepsilon) = \varepsilon/8\pi C$. We thus find that $X(M)$ converges uniformly. Since the uniform convergence of (29.1) and (29.2) was proved on the assumption that the density $|\rho(N)| < C$ is bounded, these integrals are also continuous at points at which the function $\rho(N)$ is discontinuous. Points on the boundary of the region may be looked upon as points of discontinuity in the density $\rho(N)$ which is equal to zero outside $D$. It follows that the potential $v(M)$ and the integrals $X(M)$, $Y(M)$ and $Z(M)$ are continuous in all space.

It remains to show that the functions $X(M)$, $Y(M)$ and $Z(M)$ are the partial derivatives of $v(M)$ for points $M(x, y, z) \in D$, i.e.

$$X = \frac{\partial v}{\partial x}, \quad Y = \frac{\partial v}{\partial y}, \quad z = \frac{\partial v}{\partial z}. \tag{29.3}$$

Let $(x + \Delta x, y, z)$ be the coordinates of a point $M_1$ and the running point $N(\xi, \eta, \zeta)$. Consider the difference

$$\frac{v(x + \Delta x, y, z) - v(x, y, z)}{\Delta x} - X =$$

$$= \frac{1}{\Delta x} \iiint_D \rho(N) \left( \frac{1}{r_1} - \frac{1}{r} \right) d\tau - \iiint_D \rho(N) \frac{\xi - x}{r^3} d\tau \tag{29.4}$$

We shall show that this difference tends to zero together with $\Delta x$. Let $K_{\delta_1}$ be a sphere of radius $\delta_1$ centered on $M$ and lying inside $D$, and let $D_2$ be the part of $D$ lying outside $K_{\delta_1}$. If we divide the potential $v(M)$ and the integral $X(M)$ into two parts so that

$$v(M) = \iiint_{K_{\delta_1}} \frac{\rho(N)}{r} d\tau + \iiint_{D_2} \frac{\rho(N)}{r} d\tau = v_1(M) + v_2(M),$$

$$X(M) = - \iiint_{K_{\delta_1}} \rho(N) \frac{x - \xi}{r^3} d\tau -$$

$$- \iiint_{D_2} \rho(N) \frac{x - \xi}{r^3} d\tau = X_1(M) + X_2(M).$$

then the difference (29.4) can be written in the form

$$I = \frac{v_1(x + \Delta x, y, z) - v_1(x, y, z)}{\Delta x} - X_1 +$$

$$+ \left[ \frac{v_2(x + \Delta x, y, z) - v_2(x, y, z)}{\Delta x} \right] - X_2. \tag{29.5}$$

Let us estimate each of the terms on the right-hand side of this equation, assuming that the point $M_1(x + \Delta x, y, z)$ lies inside the sphere $K_{\delta_1}$. We have

$$\frac{v_1(x + \Delta x, y, z) - v_1(x, y, z)}{\Delta x} = \frac{1}{\Delta x} \iiint\limits_{K_{\delta_1}} \rho(N) \left( \frac{1}{r_1} - \frac{1}{r} \right) d\tau;$$

and since $|r - r_1| \leqslant \Delta x$, we have

$$\left| \frac{v_1(x + \Delta x, y, z) - v_1(x, y, z)}{\Delta x} \right| \leqslant \iiint\limits_{K_{\delta_1}} \frac{|\rho(N)|}{|\Delta x|} \frac{|r - r_1|}{r \cdot r_1} \, d\tau <$$

$$< C \iiint\limits_{K_{\delta_1}} \frac{d\tau}{r r_1} \leqslant \frac{C}{2} \iiint\limits_{K_{\delta_1}} \left( \frac{1}{r^2} + \frac{1}{r_1^2} \right) d\tau. \tag{29.6}$$

Simple calculations will show that

$$\iiint\limits_{K_{\delta_1}} \frac{d\tau}{r^2} = 4\pi\delta_1, \quad \iiint\limits_{K_{\delta_1}} \frac{d\tau}{r_1^2} < \iiint\limits_{K_{2\delta_1}} \frac{d\tau}{r_1^2} = 8\pi\delta_1, \tag{29.7}$$

where $K_{2\delta_1}$ is a sphere of radius $2\delta_1$ centered on $M_1$.
From (29.6) and (29.7) we have

$$\left| \frac{v_1(x + \Delta x, y, z) - v_1(x, y, z)}{\Delta x} \right| < 6\pi\delta_1. \tag{29.8}$$

Moreover,

$$|X_1| = \left| \iiint\limits_{K_{\delta_1}} \rho(N) \, \frac{x - \xi}{r^3} \, d\tau \right| <$$

$$< C \int\limits_0^{\delta_1} \int\limits_0^{2\pi} \int\limits_0^{\pi} \sin\theta \, d\theta \, d\varphi \, dr = 4\pi C \delta_1. \tag{29.9}$$

If, now, $\varepsilon$ is a small given positive number, and if we take $\delta_1$ to be small enough so that

$$6\pi C \delta_1 < \frac{\varepsilon}{3}. \tag{29.10}$$

we have

$$\left| \frac{v_1(x + \Delta x, y, z) - v_1(x, y, z)}{\Delta x} - X_1 \right| < \frac{\varepsilon}{3} + \frac{\varepsilon}{3} = \frac{2\varepsilon}{3} \tag{29.11}$$

for all points $M_1$ lying inside $K_{\delta_1}$. For the third term in (29.5) we have

$$\lim_{\Delta x \to 0} \frac{v_2(x + \Delta x, y, z) - v_2(x, y, z)}{\Delta x} = X_2,$$

since $M_1$ and $M$ lie outside $D_2$. Consequently, for any $\varepsilon > 0$, we can find $\delta_2$ such that

$$\left| \frac{v_2(x + \Delta x, y, z) - v_2(x, y, z)}{\Delta x} - X_2 \right| < \frac{\varepsilon}{3}, \tag{29.12}$$

provided only that $|\Delta x| < \delta_2$. Finally, if we take $\delta = \min \{\delta_1, \delta_2\}$, we have from (29.5), (29.11), and (29.12)

$$\left| \frac{v(x + \Delta x, y, z) - v(x, y, z)}{\Delta x} - X \right| < \varepsilon \text{ if } |\Delta x| < \delta.$$

We have thus shown that $\partial v/\partial x = X$. Similarly, it may be shown that $\partial v/\partial y = Y$ and $\partial v/\partial z = Z$.

*Theorem 2. If the density $\rho(N)$ is continuous in a closed domain $\bar{D}$, and has continuous first-order derivatives inside $D$, then the volume integral given by (29.1) has continuous second order derivatives inside $D$ and satisfies Poisson's equation*

$$\Delta v(M) = - 4\pi\rho(M). \tag{29.13}$$

*inside $D$.*

*Proof.* Let us take an arbitrary point $M_0(x_0, y_0, z_0)$ inside $D$ and let $K_\delta$ be a sphere of radius $\delta$ which is centered on $M_0$ and lies wholly inside $D$. If $D_1$ is the part of $D$ which lies outside $K_\delta$ so that $D = D_1 + K_\delta$ let us take (29.1) in two parts:

$$v(M) = \iiint\limits_{D_1} \frac{\rho(N)}{r} \, d\tau +$$

$$+ \iiint\limits_{K_\delta} \frac{\rho(N)}{r} \, d\tau = v_1(M) + v_0(M). \tag{29.14}$$

From theorem 1 we have

$$\frac{\partial v(M)}{\partial x} = \iiint\limits_{D_1} \rho(N) \frac{\partial}{\partial x}\left(\frac{1}{r}\right) d\tau + \iiint\limits_{K_\delta} \rho(N) \frac{\partial}{\partial x}\left(\frac{1}{r}\right) d\tau,$$

but since

$$\frac{\partial \frac{1}{r}}{\partial x} = -\frac{\partial \frac{1}{r}}{\partial \xi} \qquad (r = \sqrt{(x-\xi)^2 + (y-\eta)^2 + (z-\zeta)^2}).$$

we have

$$\frac{\partial v(M)}{\partial x} = \iiint\limits_{D_1} \rho(N) \frac{\partial}{\partial x}\left(\frac{1}{r}\right) d\tau - \iiint\limits_{K_\delta} \rho(N) \frac{\partial}{\partial \xi}\left(\frac{1}{r}\right) d\tau.$$

Integrating the last integral by parts, we have

$$\frac{\partial v(M)}{\partial x} = \iiint\limits_{D_1} \rho(N) \frac{\partial}{\partial x}\left(\frac{1}{r}\right) d\tau +$$

$$+ \iiint\limits_{K_\delta} \frac{\partial \rho(N)}{\partial \xi} \frac{1}{r} d\tau - \iint\limits_{S_\delta} \frac{\rho(N) \text{ cis } (\mathbf{n}\xi)}{r} dS, \quad (29.15)$$

where $S_\delta$ is the surface of the sphere $K_\delta$ and $\mathbf{n}$ is the direction of the outward normal $2S_\delta$ at the point $M$. The first term on the right of (29.15) is a proper integral for points $M$ lying inside $K_\delta$, and has derivatives of all orders inside $K_\delta$. This is also valid for the third term, since the point $N$ lies on the surface $S_\delta$, while the point $M$ lies inside $K_\delta$. The second term is the potential due to a volume distribution with the continuous density $\partial\rho(N)/\partial\xi$, and in view of theorem 1 it has continuous first order derivatives in all space. We may therefore conclude that $\partial v(M)/\partial x$ has continuous second order derivatives inside $K_\delta$. Since $M_0$ is an arbitrary point inside $D$, we may conclude that $\partial v(M)/\partial x$ has continuous first order derivatives inside $D$. By applying a similar argument to $\partial v(M)/\partial y$ and $\partial v(M)/\partial z$, we may show that $v(M)$ has continuous second order derivatives inside $D$.

We shall now show that the volume integral $v(M)$ satisfies the Poisson equation in $D$. Let us return again to (29.14) and (29.15).

The potential $v_1(M)$ due to the volume distribution in $D_1$ is a harmonic function inside $K_\delta$ since the latter lies outside $D_1$, i.e. $\Delta v_1(M) = 0$ inside $K_\delta$ and consequently $\Delta v(M) = \Delta v_0(M)$ inside $K_\delta$. Therefore, in order to obtain $\Delta v(M)$ it is sufficient to differentiate with respect to $x$ under the integral sign those terms in (29.15) in which the integration is carried out over $K_\delta$ and $S$. Analogous expressions can be obtained for the second order derivatives with respect to $y$ and $z$. If we determine $\Delta v(M)$ in $K_\delta$ in this way, and take its value at the center $M_0(x_0, y_0, z_0)$ of the sphere $K_\delta$, we obtain

$$\Delta v(M_0) = \int\int\int_{K_\delta} \left[ \frac{\partial \rho(N)}{\partial \xi} \frac{\xi - x_0}{r_0^3} + \frac{\partial \rho(N)}{\partial \eta} \frac{\eta - y_0}{r_0^3} + \right.$$
$$\left. + \frac{\partial \rho(N)}{\partial \zeta} \frac{\zeta - z_0}{r_0^3} \right] d\tau - \int\int_{S_\delta} \rho(N) \left[ \frac{\xi - x_0}{r_0^3} \cos(\mathbf{n}\xi) + \right.$$
$$\left. + \frac{\eta - y_0}{r_0^3} \cos(\mathbf{n}\eta) + \frac{\zeta - z_0}{r_0^3} \cos(\mathbf{n}\zeta) \right] dS, \qquad (29.16)$$

where

$$r_0 = \sqrt{(x_0 + \xi)^2 + (y_0 - \eta)^2 + (z_0 - \zeta)^2}.$$

The formula given by (29.16) is valid for any $\delta$ provided only $K_\delta$ lies inside $D$ and the magnitude of $\Delta v(M_0)$ is clearly independent of the choice of $\delta$. We shall show that as $\delta$ tends to zero the triple integral will also tend to zero. In fact, let

$$m = \max \left| \frac{\partial \rho(N)}{\partial \xi} \right|$$

in a fixed small sphere $K_{\delta_0}$ so that when $\delta \leqslant \delta_0$ and since $|\xi - x_0|/r_0 \leqslant 1$, we have

$$\left| \int\int\int_{K_\delta} \frac{\partial \rho(N)}{\partial \xi} \frac{\xi - x_0}{r_0^3} d\tau \right| \leqslant m \int\int\int_{K_\delta} \frac{d\tau}{r_0^2}.$$

In terms of spherical polars with the origin at $M_0$ we have

$$\left| \int\int\int_{K_\delta} \frac{\partial \rho(N)}{\partial \xi} \frac{\xi - x_0}{r_0^3} d\tau \right| \leqslant \int_0^\delta \int_0^\pi \int_0^{2\pi} \sin\theta \, dr \, d\theta \, d\varphi = 4\pi m \delta.$$

The remaining terms in the triple integral can be estimated in a similar way. It follows that the triple integral in (29.16) tends to zero as $\delta \to 0$.

Consider now the integral over the sphere $S_\delta$ in (29.16). Since the outward normal $n$ lies along the radius of $S_\delta$ we have

$$\frac{\xi - x_0}{r_0^3} \cos(n\xi) + \frac{\eta - y_0}{r_0^3} \cos(n\eta) + \frac{\zeta - z_0}{r_0^3} \cos(n\zeta) =$$

$$= \frac{1}{r_0^2} [\cos^2(n\xi) + \cos^2(n\eta) + \cos^2(n\zeta)] = \frac{1}{r_0^2}$$

and therefore the integral over $S_\delta$ may be written in the form

$$\frac{1}{\delta^2} \int\int_{S_\delta} \rho(N)\, dS.$$

If we apply the mean value theorem to this we obtain

$$\frac{1}{\delta^2} \int\int_{S_\delta} \rho(N)\, dS = 4\pi\rho(N_\delta),$$

where $N_\delta$ is a point on $S_\delta$. As $\delta \to 0$ the point $N_\delta$ tends to $M_0$ and the integral over $S_\delta$ tends to $4\pi\rho(M_0)$. Therefore, in the limit as $\delta \to 0$, from (29.16) we have

$$\Delta v(M_0) = -4\pi\rho(M_0),$$

which was to be proved.

*Remark.* If $f(M)$ is continuous in the closed domain $D$ and has continuous first-order derivatives in $D$, then the Poisson equation

$$\Delta v(M) = -f(M)$$

has the special solution

$$v(M) = \frac{1}{4\pi} \int\int\int_D \frac{f(N)}{r}\, d\tau \qquad (r = |MN|).$$

## § 30. Lyapunov's surfaces

In order to establish rigorously the properties of the potentials due to a simple and a double layer, it is necessary to impose a number of requirements on the surfaces on which these layers are distributed.

We shall refer to a closed surface $S$ as a *Lyapunov surface* if the following three conditions are satisfied.

(1) A tangent plane to $S$ exists at each point on $S$.

(2) There exists a number $d > 0$ which is the same for all points on the surface and is such that if $N_0$ is any point on $S$, then any sphere of radius $d$ or less and centered on $N_0$ divides $S$ into two parts, one of which lies inside, and the other outside the sphere, and straight lines parallel to the normal to $S$ at $N_0$ intersect that part of $S$ which lies inside the sphere at not more than one point.

(3) If $\theta$ is an acute angle between the normals to $S$ at two points $N_1$ and $N_2$ on $S$ and if $r_{12}$ is the distance between these two points, then there exist two positive numbers $a$ and $\alpha$ $(0 \leqslant \alpha < 1)$ which are independent of the choice of $N_1$ and $N_2$ and are such that

$$\theta \leqslant ar_{21}^{\alpha} \tag{30.1}$$

for any $N_1$ and $N_2$ on $S$.

The condition given by (1) ensures that it is possible at each point $N_0$ on a Lyapunov surface to construct a local cartesian system of coordinates $X$, $Y$, $Z$ by taking the point $N_0$ as the origin of the coordinate system and the tangent plane at $N_0$ as the $XY$-plane, the normal at $N_0$ serving as the $Z$-axis. Condition (2) shows that in this local set of coordinates the equation of the part of the surface $S$ which lies inside the sphere $C_0$ of radius $d$ and centered on $N_0$ can be written in the explicit form

$$\zeta = f(\xi, \eta). \tag{30.2}$$

Henceforth, we shall take $(\xi, \eta, \zeta)$ as the coordinates of a variable point $N$ on $S$ and $(x, y, z)$ as the coordinates of any point $M$ in space. From condition (3) it follows that the partial derivatives $f'_\xi$, $f'_\eta$ whose existence is ensured by condition (1) are continuous functions of $\xi$ and $\eta$. We shall suppose that $\delta$ is small enough, for example we may suppose that

$$ad^\alpha \leqslant 1, \tag{30.3}$$

so that the angle $\theta_0$ between the normal at $N_0$ and the normal at any point $N$ on a piece of $S$ lying inside the sphere $C_0$ does not reach $\pi/2$. Let $r_0$ be the distance $|\overline{N_0 N}|$ ($r_0 \leqslant d$). We have

$$\cos \theta_0 \geqslant 1 - \tfrac{1}{2}\theta_0^2 \geqslant 1 - \tfrac{1}{2}a^2 r_0^{2\alpha}, \tag{30.4}$$

and hence

$$\frac{1}{\cos \theta_0} = \sqrt{1 + f_\xi^2 + f_\eta^2} \leqslant 1 + a^2 r_0^{2\alpha} \leqslant 2 \tag{30.5}$$

so that, in view of (30.3)

$$f_\xi^2 + f_\eta^2 \leqslant 2a^2 r_0^{2\alpha} + a^4 r_0^{4\alpha} \leqslant 3a^2 r_0^{2\alpha} \tag{30.6}$$

and

$$|f_\xi| \leqslant \sqrt{3} a r_0^\alpha, \quad |f_\eta| \leqslant \sqrt{3} a r_0^\alpha. \tag{30.7}$$

If we substitute

$$\xi = \rho_0 \cos \vartheta, \quad \eta = \rho_0 \sin \vartheta \qquad (\rho_0 = \sqrt{\xi^2 + \eta^2}),$$

we obtain

$$\zeta_{\rho_0}^2 = (f_\xi \cos \vartheta + f_\eta \sin \vartheta)^2 \leqslant f_\xi^2 + f_\eta^2,$$

and hence, in view of (30.6),

$$|\zeta_{\rho_0}| \leqslant \sqrt{3} a r_0^\alpha, \tag{30.8}$$

or, very approximately,

$$|\zeta_{\rho_0}| \leqslant \sqrt{3} \qquad (a r_0^\alpha \leqslant 1).$$

Hence,

$$|\zeta| \leqslant \sqrt{3} \rho_0, \tag{30.9}$$

but

$$r_0 \leqslant \sqrt{\rho_0^2 + \zeta^2} \leqslant 2\rho_0. \tag{30.10}$$

From (30.8) we have

$$|\zeta_{\rho_0}| \leqslant \sqrt{3}a2^\alpha\rho_0^\alpha,$$

and hence

$$|\zeta| \leqslant \frac{\sqrt{3}\cdot2^\alpha}{\alpha+1}\, a\rho_0^{\alpha+1},$$

or, even more so,

$$|\zeta| \leqslant 2a\rho_0^{\alpha+1},$$

since $2^\alpha \leqslant \alpha + 1$ when $\alpha \leqslant 1$. From (30.4) and (30.10) we have

$$1 - \cos\theta_0 \leqslant \tfrac{1}{2}a^2r_0^{2\alpha} \leqslant 2^{2\alpha-1}a^2\rho_0^{2\alpha}.$$

From (30.7) and (30.10) we have

$$|\cos(\boldsymbol{n}X)| = \frac{|f_\xi|}{\sqrt{1+f_\xi^2+f_\eta^2}} < |f_\xi| \leqslant \sqrt{3}ar_0^\alpha \leqslant \sqrt{3}\cdot2^\alpha a\rho_0^\alpha.$$

and similarly

$$|\cos(\boldsymbol{n}Y)| < \sqrt{3}\cdot2^\alpha a\rho_0^\alpha.$$

Moreover,

$$\cos(\boldsymbol{n}Z) = \cos\theta_0$$

and, in view of (30.5)

$$|\cos(\boldsymbol{n}Z)| \geqslant \tfrac{1}{2}.$$

Let us now write down all the systems which we have obtained above:

$$|\zeta| \leqslant C\rho_0^{\alpha+1}, \quad |\cos(\boldsymbol{n}X)| \leqslant C\rho^\alpha, \quad |\cos(\boldsymbol{n}Y)| \leqslant C\rho^\alpha,$$
$$1 - \cos(\boldsymbol{n}Z) \leqslant C\rho_0^{2\alpha}, \quad |\cos(\boldsymbol{n}Z)| \geqslant \tfrac{1}{2}, \qquad (30.11)$$

where $C$ is the maximum constant among those entering into the above inequalities. It is evident that these results are valid if $\rho_0$ is replaced by $r_0$ on the right-hand sides.

## § 31. Potential due to a double layer

Consider the potential due to a double layer of continuous density $\mu(N)$ distributed on the Lyapunov surface:

$$w(M) = - \iint\limits_{S} \mu(N) \frac{\partial}{\partial n} \left( \frac{1}{r} \right) dS = \iint\limits_{S} \mu(N) \frac{\cos \varphi}{r^2} dS, \quad (31.1)$$

where the derivative is taken along the outward normal $\boldsymbol{n}$ to the surface $S$ at the point $N(\xi, \eta, \zeta)$ and the vector $\boldsymbol{r}$ is drawn from $M(x, y, z)$ to $N(\xi, \eta, \zeta)$, $\varphi$ being the angle between $\boldsymbol{r}$ and $\boldsymbol{n}$.

Outside $S$ the potential due to a double layer has derivatives of all orders and satisfies the Laplace equation. We shall show that the potential due to the double layer tends to zero at infinity. Let us take the origin inside a finite domain $D$ bounded by a surface $S$. We then have $MN \geqslant OM - ON$ or $r \geqslant R - ON$. Let $L$ be the greatest distance between points on the surface and the origin. We then have $r \geqslant R - L$. We shall suppose that $M$ is far enough from the origin so that $R < 2L$, i.e. $L > \frac{1}{2}R$ so that $r > \frac{1}{2}R$ or $1/r < 2/R$. We now have

$$|w(M)| \leqslant \iint\limits_{S} |\mu(N)| \frac{|\cos \varphi|}{r^2} dS <$$

$$< \frac{4}{R^2} \iint\limits_{S} |\mu(N)| dS = \frac{A}{R^2},$$

where

$$A = 4 \iint\limits_{S} |\mu(N)| dS.$$

In other words, the potential due to a double layer tends to zero at infinity as $1/R^2$.

Suppose now that the point $M$ coincides with a point $N_0$ on the surface $S$. The distance $r_0 = \overline{|N_0 N|}$ will vanish when $N$ and $N_0$ coincide and the integral in (31.1) will then be improper. We shall show that it converges. To establish this, it is sufficient to consider the integrand on a piece $S_0$ of the surface $S$ which lies inside the sphere $C_0$ of radius $d$ and centered on $N_0$. On the remaining part of the surface the integral has a finite value (the point $N_0$ lies outside the region of integration).

If we construct the local system of coordinates at the point $N_0$, the equation of the piece $\sigma_0$ of the surface $S$ can be written in the form

$$\zeta = f(\xi, \eta).$$

In the local system of coordinates the point $N_0$ has the coordinates $(0, 0, 0)$, while $N$ has the coordinates $(\xi, \eta, \zeta)$ and

$$r_0 = |\overline{N_0 N}| = \sqrt{\xi^2 + \eta^2 + \zeta^2}.$$

Let us now find the expression for $\cos \varphi_0 = \cos (r_0, n)$ where $r_0$ is the direction of $\overline{N_0 N}$:

$$\cos \varphi_0 = \cos (r_0 X) \cos (nX) + \cos (r_0 Y) \cos (nY) +$$
$$+ \cos (r_0 Z) \cos (nZ),$$

but

$$\cos (r_0 X) = \frac{\xi}{r_0}, \quad \cos (r_0 Y) = \frac{\eta}{r_0}, \quad \cos (r_0 Z) = \frac{\zeta}{r_0}.$$

and therefore

$$\cos \varphi_0 = \frac{\xi}{r_0} \cos (nX) + \frac{\eta}{r_0} \cos (nY) + \frac{\zeta}{r_0} \cos (nZ).$$

In view of (30.11) and the obvious inequalities

$$|\xi| \leqslant \rho_0, \quad |\eta| \leqslant \rho_0, \quad \rho_0 \leqslant r_0 \qquad (\rho_0 = \sqrt{\xi^2 + \eta^2}),$$

we obtain

$$\left| \frac{\cos \varphi_0}{r_0^2} \right| \leqslant \frac{3C\rho_0^\alpha}{\rho_0^2} = \frac{b}{\rho_0^{2-\alpha}}, \tag{31.2}$$

where $b$ is a constant. Moreover, for a continuous function we have

$$|\mu(N)| \leqslant A \qquad (N \in S). \tag{31.3}$$

If we replace the integral over $\sigma_0$ by an integral over the projection $\sigma_0'$ of $\sigma_0$ on to the $XY$-plane of the local system of coordinates, we obtain

$$\iint\limits_{\sigma} \mu(N) \frac{\cos\varphi_0}{r_0^2}\, dS = \iint\limits_{\sigma_0'} \mu(\xi,\eta) \frac{\cos\varphi_0}{r_0^2}\, \frac{d\xi\, d\eta}{\cos\theta_0}.$$

In view of (30.11) and (31.2) and (31.3) we have

$$\left| \mu(\xi,\eta) \frac{\cos\varphi_0}{r_0^2}\, \frac{1}{\cos\theta_0} \right| \leqslant \frac{2Ab}{\rho_0^{2-\alpha}},$$

from which we deduce the convergence of (31.1) provided $M$ lies on $S$. It follows that the potential (31.1) due to a double layer is determined in all space.

If the point $M$ lies on $S$, for example it coincides with $N_0$ on $S$, then the value of (31.1) at this point is called the *direct value* of the potential of the double layer. Suppose now that the point $M(x, y, z)$ lies outside $S$ and approaches $N_0 \in S$. If at the same time it is found that the potential of the double layer $w(M)$ tends to a finite limit, then we shall say that the potential of the double layer assumes the *limiting value* at $N_0$. The limiting and direct values will not in general be the same. Moreover, we shall show that the limiting values of the potential $w(M)$ of a double layer are in general different, depending on whether the point $M$ approaches the surface $S$ from outside or from inside, and that these limiting values are different from the direct values, i.e. we shall show that the potential (31.1) undergoes a discontinuity on passing through $S$.

Consider the potential (31.1) when $\mu(N) \equiv 1$. Under these conditions

$$w_1(M) = - \iint\limits_{S} \frac{\partial\, \dfrac{1}{r}}{\partial n}\, dS = \iint\limits_{S} \frac{\cos\varphi}{r^2}\, dS. \qquad (31.4)$$

If the point $M$ lies outside * the closed surface $S$, then $1/r$ is the harmonic function inside $S$ and has continuous derivatives of all

---

* We shall say that $M$ lies inside (outside) a closed surface $S$ if it belongs to a finite domain $D_i$ (infinite domain $D_e$) bounded by this surface.

orders right up to $S$. Moreover, in view of (19.2)

$$w_1(M) = -\iint_S \frac{\partial \frac{1}{r}}{\partial n} dS = 0 \qquad (M \text{ outside } S).$$

Let us suppose now that $M$ lies outside $S$ and let us consider a small sphere $C_\rho$ centered on $M$ and having a radius $\rho$. In the space $D'$ between $C_\rho$ and $S$ the function $1/r$ is harmonic and

$$\iint_S \frac{\partial \frac{1}{r}}{\partial n} dS + \iint_{C_\rho} \frac{\partial \frac{1}{r}}{\partial n} dS = 0.$$

On the sphere $C_\rho$ the outward normal is opposite to the radius of the sphere and therefore

$$\frac{\partial \frac{1}{r}}{\partial n}\bigg|_{C_\rho} = -\frac{\partial \frac{1}{r}}{\partial r}\bigg|_{C_\rho} = \frac{1}{\rho^2},$$

so that the preceding formula may be written in the form

$$\iint_S \frac{\partial \frac{1}{r}}{\partial n} dS + \frac{1}{\rho^2} \iint_{C_\rho} dS = 0$$

or

$$\iint_S \frac{\partial \frac{1}{r}}{\partial n} dS + 4\pi = 0,$$

and hence

$$w_1(M) = -\iint_S \frac{\partial \frac{1}{r}}{\partial n} dS = 4\pi \qquad (M \text{ inside } S).$$

Finally, let us suppose that $M$ lies on the surface $S$ and let us determine the direct value of the potential (31.4). Let us draw a small sphere $C_\rho$ centered on $M$ and having a radius $\rho \leqslant d$. This sphere will cut a part $\sigma$ of $S$. The remainder of the surface will be denoted by $S - \sigma$. By definition of improper integrals we have

$$\lim_{\rho \to 0} \int\int_{S-\sigma} \frac{\partial \frac{1}{r}}{\partial n} \, dS = \int\int_{S} \frac{\partial \frac{1}{r}}{\partial n} \, dS. \tag{31.5}$$

Let $C'_\rho$ be the part of $C_\rho$ which lies inside $S$ and let us consider the space between $S - \sigma$ and $C'_\rho$. Since $M$ lies outside this region, it follows that inside this region $1/r$ is harmonic, and consequently

$$\int\int_{S-\sigma} \frac{\partial \frac{1}{r}}{\partial n} \, dS + \int\int_{C_\rho'} \frac{\partial \frac{1}{r}}{\partial n} \, dS_\rho = 0$$

or, using (31.5), we have

$$\int\int_{S} \frac{\partial \frac{1}{r}}{\partial n} \, dS = - \lim_{\rho \to 0} \int\int_{C_\rho'} \frac{\partial \frac{1}{r}}{\partial n} \, dS_\rho. \tag{31.6}$$

Let us introduce spherical polars with the origin at $M$. As before, we have

$$\left. \frac{\partial \frac{1}{r}}{\partial n} \right|_{C_\rho} = \frac{1}{\rho^2}$$

and

$$dS_\rho = \rho^2 \sin\theta \, d\theta \, d\varphi,$$

so that

$$\int\int_{C_\rho'} \frac{\partial \frac{1}{r}}{\partial n} \, dS_\rho = \int_0^{2\pi} \int_{\theta(\varphi)}^{\pi} \sin\theta \, d\theta \, d\varphi =$$

$$= \int_0^{2\pi} [1 + \cos\theta(\varphi)] \, d\varphi = 2\pi + \int_0^{2\pi} \cos\theta(\varphi) \, d\varphi. \tag{31.7}$$

We shall show that

$$\lim_{\rho \to 0} \int_0^{2\pi} \cos \theta(\varphi) \, d\varphi = 0.$$

Let us introduce the local system of coordinates with the origin at $M$ and let the $Z$-axis lie along the normal to $S$ at $M$ and the $XY$-plane be tangent to $S$ at $M$. We then have $\cos \theta(\varphi) = \zeta/\rho$. We note that the points $\{\rho, \varphi, \theta(\varphi)\}$ lie on the line of intersection of the sphere $C_\rho$ with the Lyapunov surface $S$, and therefore the coordinates $\zeta$ of points on this line are such that $|\zeta| \leqslant C\rho^{1+\alpha}$. Consequently

$$|\cos \theta(\varphi)| \leqslant C\rho^\alpha,$$

from which it follows that $\cos \theta(\varphi) \to 0$ uniformly as $\rho \to \infty$, i.e. independently of the point $M$ and

$$\int_0^{2\pi} \cos \theta(\varphi) \, d\varphi \to 0$$

when $\rho \to 0$. It follows that, using (31.7), we have

$$\lim_{\rho \to 0} \int \int_{C_\rho'} \frac{\partial \frac{1}{r}}{\partial n} \, dS_\rho = 2\pi$$

and finally, from (31.6) we obtain

$$\int \int_S \frac{\partial \frac{1}{r}}{\partial n} \, dS = -2\pi \quad (M \text{ lies on } S).$$

Therefore,

$$w_1(M) = -\int \int_S \frac{\partial \frac{1}{r}}{\partial n} \, dS = \begin{cases} 0 & (M \text{ outside } S), \\ 2\pi & (M \text{ on } S), \\ 4\pi & (M \text{ inside } S). \end{cases} \quad (31.8)$$

The integral $w_1(M)$ is known as Gauss's integral and is a discontinuous function.

Henceforth, we shall suppose that the surface $S$ is such that for any position of the point $M$ we have the inequality

$$\int\int_S \frac{|\cos\varphi|}{r^2}\, dS \leqslant K, \qquad (31.9)$$

where $K$ is a given positive number.

The formulae in (31.8) show that when $\mu(N) \equiv 1$ the potential due to a double layer undergoes a discontinuity when the point cuts the surface $S$. We shall show that this also occurs for an arbitrary discontinuity in the density $\mu(N)$.

*Theorem. The potential $w(M)$ due to a double layer tends to different limits as the point $M$ tends to the point $N_0$ on the surface $S$ depending on whether the approach is made from outside or from inside. If $M$ approaches $N_0$ from outside, then the limit is $w_e(N_0)$, whilst in the opposite case it is $w_i(N_0)$, where*

$$w_e(N_0) = \int\int_S \mu(N) \frac{\cos\varphi_0}{r_0^2}\, dS - 2\pi\mu(N_0) =$$

$$= w(N_0) - 2\pi\mu(N_0), \qquad (31.10)$$

$$w_i(N_0) = \int\int_S \mu(N) \frac{\cos\varphi_0}{r_0^2}\, dS + 2\pi\mu(N_0) =$$

$$= w(N_0) + 2\pi\mu(N_0).$$

In these expressions $\varphi_0$ is the angle between $r_0 = \overline{N_0 N}$ and the outward normal $n$ to $S$ at the running point $N$.

*Proof.* Let $N_0$ be a fixed point on $S$. The potential $w(M)$ due to the double layer can be written in the form

$$w(M) = \int\int_S [\mu(N) - \mu(N_0)] \frac{\cos\varphi}{r^2}\, dS + \mu(N_0)\int\int_S \frac{\cos\varphi}{r^2}\, dS =$$

$$= w_0(M) + \mu(N_0)w_1(M). \qquad (31.11)$$

Let us suppose that $M$ tends to $N_0$ either from the outside or from the inside of $S$. The behaviour of $w_1(M)$ is known – it is given by Gauss's theorem. Consider the potential $w_0(M)$ of the double layer. We shall show that the latter remains continuous when $M$ cuts $S$ at $N_0$. Suppose that $\varepsilon > 0$ is a given number. Since $\mu(N)$ is continuous, we can find a part $\sigma_0$ of the surface $S$ which contains $N_0$ and on which

$$|\mu(N) - \mu(N_0)| \leqslant \frac{\varepsilon}{4K}, \qquad (31.12)$$

where $K$ is the constant in (31.9). If we divide $S$ into two parts, say $\sigma_0$ and $S - \sigma_0$, we can write

$$w_0(M) = w_0^{(1)}(M) + w_0^{(2)}(M), \qquad (31.13)$$

where

$$w_0^{(1)}(M) = \iint\limits_{\sigma_0} [\mu(N) - \mu(N_0)] \frac{\cos \varphi}{r^2} dS,$$

$$w_0^{(2)}(M) = \iint\limits_{S-\sigma_0} [\mu(N) - \mu(N_0)] \frac{\cos \varphi}{r^2} dS. \qquad (31.14)$$

For any $M$ we have

$$|w_0^{(1)}(M)| \leqslant \iint\limits_{\sigma_0} |\mu(N) - \mu(N_0)| \frac{|\cos \varphi|}{r^2} dS,$$

and hence, in view of (31.9) and (31.12),

$$|w_0^{(1)}(M)| \leqslant \frac{\varepsilon}{4}. \qquad (31.15)$$

From (31.13) it follows that

$$w_0(M) - w_0(N_0) = w_0^{(1)}(M) - w_0^{(1)}(N_0) + w_0^{(2)}(M) - w_0^{(2)}(N_0),$$

and hence

$$|w_0(M) - w_0(N_0)| \leqslant |w_0^{(1)}(M)| +$$
$$+ |w_0^{(1)}(N_0)| + |w_0^{(2)}(M) - w_0^{(2)}(N_0)|$$

or, in view of (31.15),

$$|w_0(M) - w_0(N_0)| \leqslant \frac{\varepsilon}{2} + |w_0^{(2)}(M) - w_0^{(2)}(N_0)|. \qquad (31.16)$$

In the potential due to the double layer, $w_0^{(2)}(M)$, the integration is carried out over $S - \sigma_0$ and the point $N_0$ lies inside $\sigma_0$ so that the function $w_0^{(2)}(M)$ is continuous at $N_0$ and its immediate neighbourhood.

Therefore, for all $M$ close enough to $N_0$ we have

$$|w_0^{(2)}(M) - w_0^{(2)}(N_0)| < \frac{\varepsilon}{2}$$

and, in view of (31.16),

$$|w_0(M) - w_0(N_0)| < \varepsilon,$$

from which it follows that since $\varepsilon > 0$ is arbitrary, the function $w_0(M)$ must be continuous at $N_0$. Thus,

$$\lim_{M \to N_0} w_0(M) = w_0(N_0). \tag{31.17}$$

Suppose that $M$ tends to $N_0$ from inside the surface $S$. Under these conditions we have from (31.8), (31.17) and (31.11)

$$\lim_{M \to N_0} w(M) = w_0(N_0) + 4\pi\mu(N_0). \tag{31.18}$$

Suppose now that the point $M$ coincides with the point $N_0$ on $S$ in equation (31.11). In view of (31.8) we then have

$$w(N_0) = w_0(N_0) + 2\pi\mu(N_0). \tag{31.19}$$

and comparison of this with (31.18) yields

$$w_i(N_0) = w(N_0) + 2\pi\mu(N_0). \tag{31.20}$$

Suppose now that $M$ tends to $N_0$ from outside the surface $S$. In the same way we can show that

$$\lim_{M \to N_0} w(M) = w_e(N_0) = w_0(N_0),$$

and hence, in view of (31.19), we have

$$w_e(N_0) = w(N_0) - 2\pi\mu(N_0). \tag{31.21}$$

From (31.20) and (31.21) we have at once that the change in the potential due to the double layer at any point $N_0$ on $S$ is given by

$$w_i(N_0) - w_e(N_0) = 4\pi\mu(N_0). \tag{31.22}$$

*Remark.* Suppose that the point $M$ lies on $S$, and let us denote it by $N$. From (31.11) and (31.8), we then have

$$w(N) = w_0(N) + 2\pi\mu(N_0).$$

Let us now allow $N$ to move towards $N_0$ along the surface $S$. Since $w_0(N)$ is continuous, we shall have

$$\lim_{N \to N_0} w(N) = w_0(N_0) + 2\pi\mu(N_0).$$

Comparison of this with (31.19) yields

$$\lim_{N \to N_0} w(N) = w(N_0),$$

and hence it follows that the potential $w(M)$ due to a double layer is continuous on $S$. In view of (31.10) and the continuity of $w(N_0)$ as $N_0$ moves over $S$, we may conclude that the potential $w(M)$ of a double layer is continuous inside $S$ and right up to $S$. In the same way, we can show that it is continuous outside $S$ and right up to the latter.

## § 32. Potential due to a simple layer

Consider the potential due to a simple layer of continuous density $\mu_N$ on a Lyapunov surface:

$$u(M) = \int\int_S \frac{\mu(N)}{r}\, dS \qquad (r = |\overline{MN}|). \tag{32.1}$$

At all points $N(x, y, z)$ of space which do not belong to $S$ this potential has derivatives of any order and satisfies the Laplace equation. As in § 31, it may be shown that this potential tends to zero at infinity as $1/R$ where $R = \sqrt{x^2 + y^2 + z^2}$.

*Theorem. The potential due to a simple layer of continuous density is a continuous function in all space.*

*Proof.* The potential $u(M)$ of a simple layer is continuous at point $M$ not belonging to the surface $S$. We shall show that $u(M)$ is also continuous on $S$. To do this, we must show that the integral (32.1) converges uniformly at points on $S$. Let $N_0$ be an arbitrary point on $S$, and let us take it as the origin of the local system of coordinates.

Suppose that $\varepsilon > 0$ is a given number and $\sigma_1$ is the part of $S$ defined by the condition

$$\xi^2 + \eta^2 \leqslant d_1^2 \qquad (d_1 \leqslant d/4).$$

We shall show that $d_1$ can be chosen to be so small that for any position of $M$ in the neighbourhood of $N_0$ we have

$$\left| \iint_{\sigma_1} \frac{\mu(N)}{r} \, dS \right| \leqslant \varepsilon. \tag{32.2}$$

We have

$$\left| \iint_{\sigma_1} \frac{\mu(N)\, dS}{r} \right| \leqslant 2A \iint_{\sigma_1'} \frac{d\xi \, d\eta}{\rho_1}, \tag{32.3}$$

where $\sigma_1'$ is a circle of radius $d_1$ centered on $N_0$, $\rho_1$ is the length of the projection $M_1 N_1$ of the segment $MN$ on to the tangent plane $2S$ at $N_0$, and $|\mu(N)| \leqslant A$. We shall suppose that $M$ lies inside the sphere of radius $d_1$ centered on $N_0$. The point $M_1$ will then belong to the circle $\sigma_1'$ and if we take on the plane $(\xi, \eta)$ a circle $\sigma_1''$ of radius $2d_1$ and centered on $M_1$, it will contain the entire circle $\sigma_1'$ so that, in view of (32.3)

$$\left| \iint_{\sigma_1} \frac{\mu(N)}{r} \, dS \right| \leqslant 2A \iint_{\rho_1 \leqslant 2d_1} \frac{d\xi \, d\eta}{\rho_1} =$$

$$= 2A \int_0^{2\pi} \int_0^{2d_1} \frac{\rho_1 \, d\rho_1 \, d\varphi}{\rho_1} = 8\pi A \, d_1.$$

This is independent of the position of $N_0$ on $S$. If we fix $d_1$ so that $8\pi A d_1 < \varepsilon$ we obtain (32.2) for any position of $M$ in a sphere of radius $d_1$ centered on $N_0$. This means that (32.1) converges uniformly at $N_0$, and therefore $u(M)$ is continuous at the point $N_0$ on $S$, which was to be proved.

Normal derivative of the potential due to a simple layer. Let $\boldsymbol{n_0}$ be the direction of the outward normal at a point $N_0$ on $S$. Let us suppose that $M$ does not lie on $S$ and let us construct the derivative of the potential (32.1) of a simple layer along the direction of $\boldsymbol{n_0}$.

The factor $1/r$ is the only one which depends on $M$ and we may differentiate under the integral sign:

$$\frac{\partial u(M)}{\partial n_0} = \iint_S \mu(N) \frac{\partial}{\partial n_0}\left(\frac{1}{r}\right) dS = \iint_S \mu(N) \frac{\cos \psi}{r^2} dS. \quad (32.4)$$

We note that the latter integral is different from the potential of a double layer as given by (31.1). In the latter expression $\varphi = (r, n)$ where $n$ is a unit vector along the outward normal at the point $N$ which is variable in the region of integration, whilst in (32.4) $\psi = (r, n_0)$ where $n_0$ is a unit vector along the outward normal at a fixed point $N_0$. In both cases $r = \overline{MN}$.

We shall show that the integral (32.4) exists even when $M$ coincides with the point $N_0$ mentioned above. In the latter case, we shall write (32.4) in the form

$$\iint_S \mu(N) \frac{\cos \psi_0}{r_0^2} dS = \iint_S \mu(N) \frac{\cos (r_0, n_0)}{r_0^2} dS, \quad (32.5)$$

where $r_0 = |\overline{N_0 N}|$ and $\psi_0 = (r_0, n_0)$ is the angle between the directions of $\overline{N_0 N}$ and $n_0$. For this it is sufficient to consider it over a part $\sigma_0$ of the surface $S$ containing $N_0$. Let us construct the local system of coordinates at the point $N_0$ and denote the coordinates of a point $M$ by $(x, y, z)$ and the coordinates at the point $N$ in the local coordinate system by $(\xi, \eta, \zeta)$. We then have

$$\iint_{\sigma_0} \mu(N) \frac{\zeta - z}{r^3} dS.$$

If $M$ coincides with $N_0$, then $z = 0$ and the integral becomes

$$\iint_{\sigma_0} \mu(N) \frac{\zeta}{r_0^3} dS = \iint_{\sigma_0'} \mu(\xi, \eta) \frac{\zeta(\xi, \eta)}{r_0^3 \cos (nz)} d\xi d\eta,$$

where $\sigma_0'$ is the projection of $\sigma_0$ onto the tangent plane from the surface $S$ at the point $N_0$ and $\zeta = \zeta(\xi, \eta)$ is the equation of the part $\sigma_0$ of the surface $S$ in the local system of coordinates. Since

$$|\zeta| \leqslant c \rho_0^{1+\alpha}, \quad |\cos (nz)| \geqslant \tfrac{1}{2},$$

we have the following estimate for the integrand:

$$r_0 \geqslant \rho_0, \quad |\mu(N)| \leqslant A,$$

$$\left| \mu(\xi, \eta) \, \frac{\zeta(\xi, \eta)}{r_0^3 \cos (\boldsymbol{n}z)} \right| \leqslant \frac{2CA}{\rho_0^{2-\alpha}}.$$

Hence, it follows that the integral given by (32.4) converges if the point $M$ coincides with $N_0$.

Let us consider now the behaviour of the normal derivative of the potential of a simple layer as given by (32.4) when $M$ approaches $N_0$ along the normal either from inside or from outside $S$. We shall show that the normal derivative for the potential of a simple layer has definite limits which are given by

$$\left( \frac{\partial u(N_0)}{\partial n_0} \right)_i = \iint\limits_S \mu(N) \, \frac{\cos \psi_0}{r_0^2} \, dS + 2\pi\mu(N_0),$$

$$\left( \frac{\partial u(N_0)}{\partial n_0} \right)_e = \iint\limits_S \mu(N) \, \frac{\cos \psi_0}{r_0^2} \, dS - 2\pi\mu(N_0).$$

$$(32.6)$$

To prove these formulae consider the difference $F(M)$ between (32.4) and the potential due to a double layer with the same density $\mu(N)$:

$$F(M) = \frac{\partial u(M)}{\partial n_0} - w(M) = \iint\limits_S \mu(N) \, \frac{\cos \psi - \cos \varphi}{r^2} \, dS.$$

$$(32.7)$$

This integral is significant if $M$ does not lie on $S$ or if $M$ coincides with the point $N_0$ on $S$. We shall show that the integral in (32.7) has a limit as $M \to N_0$ along the normal $\boldsymbol{n}_0$ and that this limit is equal to the value of the integral $F(M)$ at $M = N_0$. Let us construct the local set of coordinates at the point $N_0$. Let $\sigma_1$ be the part of the surface $S$ defined by the condition

$$\xi^2 + \eta^2 \leqslant d_1^2 (d_1 \leqslant d/2).$$

The point $M$ lies on the normal to $S$ drawn at the point $N_0$, i.e. at the local system of coordinates $x = 0$, $y = 0$; $(\xi, \zeta, \eta)$ are the coordinates of the point $N$ in the local system of coordinates. We then have

$$\cos \varphi = \frac{\xi}{r} \cos (\boldsymbol{n}X) + \frac{\eta}{r} \cos (\boldsymbol{n}Y) + \frac{\zeta - z}{r} \cos (\boldsymbol{n}z),$$

$$\cos \psi = \frac{\zeta - z}{r},$$

and, therefore,

$$\frac{\cos \psi - \cos \varphi}{r^2} =$$

$$= - \frac{\xi}{r^3} \cos (\boldsymbol{n}X) - \frac{\eta}{r^3} \cos (\boldsymbol{n}Y) - \frac{\zeta - z}{r} (\cos (\boldsymbol{n}Z) - 1).$$

Since

$$|\cos (\boldsymbol{n}X)| \leqslant C\rho_0^\alpha, \quad |\cos (\boldsymbol{n}Y)| \leqslant C\rho_0^\alpha,$$

$$1 - \cos (\boldsymbol{n}Z) \leqslant C\rho_0^{2\alpha},$$

$$|\xi| \leqslant \rho_0, \quad |\eta| \leqslant \rho_0, \quad r \geqslant \rho_0, \quad |\zeta - z| \leqslant r,$$

where $\rho_0 = \sqrt{\xi^2 + \zeta^2}$ is the length of the projection of $\overline{MN}$ onto the $XY$ plane we have

$$\frac{|\cos \psi - \cos \varphi|}{r^2} \leqslant \frac{b_1}{\rho_0^{2-\alpha}},$$

where $b_1$ is a constant. Since, moreover, $|\mu(N)| \leqslant A$, we have

$$\left| \iint_{\sigma_1} \mu(N) \frac{\cos \psi - \cos \varphi}{r^2} dS \right| \leqslant$$

$$\leqslant \iint_{\rho_0 \leqslant d_1} \frac{2Ab_1}{\rho_0^{2-\alpha}} d\xi d\eta = 2Ab_1 \int_0^{2\pi} \int_0^{d_1} \frac{d\rho_0 d\varphi}{\rho_0^{1-\alpha}} = b_2 d_1^\alpha,$$

where $b_2$ is a constant. This estimate is valid for any position of $M$ along the normal to $S$ at the point $N_0$, including the situation where $M$ coincides with $N_0$. Hence, it follows that if $\varepsilon > 0$ is given, then by fixing $d_1$ so that $b_2 d_1^\alpha < \varepsilon/4$, we shall have

$$\left| \iint_{\sigma_1} \mu(N) \frac{\cos \psi - \cos \varphi}{r^2} dS \right| \leqslant \frac{\varepsilon}{4}. \tag{32.8}$$

If we now split $S$ into the two parts $\sigma_1$ and $S - \sigma_1$ we can write

$$F(M) = F^{(1)}(M) + F^{(2)}(M), \tag{32.9}$$

where

$$F^{(1)}(M) = \iint\limits_{\sigma_1} \mu(N) \, \frac{\cos \psi - \cos \varphi}{r^2} \, dS,$$

$$F^{(2)}(M) = \iint\limits_{S - \sigma_1} \mu(N) \, \frac{\cos \psi - \cos \varphi}{r^2} \, dS.$$

From (32.9) it follows that

$$F(M) - F(N_0) = F^{(1)}(M) - F^{(1)}(N_0) + F^{(2)}(M) - F^{(2)}(N_0),$$

and hence

$$|F(M) - F(N_0)| \leqslant |F^{(1)}(M)| + |F^{(1)}(N_0)| + |F^{(2)}(M) - F^{(2)}(N_0)|$$

or in view of (32.8)

$$|F(M) - F(N_0)| \leqslant \frac{\varepsilon}{2} + |F^{(2)}(M) - F^{(2)}(N_0)|, \tag{32.10}$$

if we assume that $M$ lies on the normal to $S$ at the point $M_0$. In the integral $F^{(2)}(M)$ the integration is carried out over $S - \sigma_1$ and the point $N_0$ lies inside $\sigma_1$ and therefore the function $F^{(2)}(M)$ is continuous at $N_0$ and in its immediate neighbourhood. Therefore, for all $M$ near enough to $N_0$, we have

$$|F^{(2)}(M) - F^{(2)}(N_0)| < \frac{\varepsilon}{2}$$

and in view of (32.10)

$$|F(M) - F(N_0)| < \varepsilon,$$

Hence, it follows that since $\varepsilon > 0$ is arbitrary

$$\lim_{M \to N_0} F(M) = F(N_0), \tag{32.11}$$

where $M \to N_0$ along the normal to $S$ at $N_0$ either from inside or from outside. It has been earlier shown that the potential $w(M)$

due to a double layer tends to a limit as $M$ approaches $N_0$ either from inside or from outside $S$. In view of (32.11) it then follows from (32.7) that the normal derivative of the potential due to a single layer, given by (32.4), has definite limits as $M \to N_0$ along the normal either from inside or from outside $S$. Using (32.11) we have

$$\left( \frac{\partial u(N_0)}{\partial n_0} \right)_t - w_t(N_0) = \int\int\limits_S \mu(N) \, \frac{\cos \psi_0}{r_0^2} \, dS - w(N_0),$$

$$\left( \frac{\partial u(N_0)}{\partial n_0} \right)_e - w_e(N_0) = \int\int\limits_S \mu(N) \, \frac{\cos \psi_0}{r_0^2} \, dS - w(N_0),$$

and when (31.10) is taken into account, we obtain the expressions given by (32.6). From (32.6) it follows directly that the change in the normal derivative of the potential due to a single layer is

$$\left( \frac{\partial u(N_0)}{\partial n_0} \right)_i - \left( \frac{\partial u(N_0)}{\partial n_0} \right)_e = 4\pi\mu(N_0).$$

# LITERATURE CITED

1. SMIRNOV, V. I. Kurs Vysshei matematiki (A Course of Higher Mathematics), Vol. II–IV (Fizmatgiz, 1958–1962).
2. PETROVSKII, I. G. Lektsii ob uravneniyakh s chastnymi proizvodnymi (Lectures on Partial Differential Equations) (Fizmatgiz, 1961).
3. SOBOLEV, S. L. Uravneniya matematicheskoi fiziki (Equations of Mathematical Physics) (Gostekhizdat, 1956).
4. COURANT, R. and HILBERT, D. Methods of Mathematical Physics, Vols. I and II.
5. KOSHLYAKOV, N. S., GLINER, E. B. and SMIRNOV, M. M. Osnovnye differentsial'nye uravneniya matematicheskoy fiziki (Basic Differential Equations of Mathematical Physics) (Fizmatgiz, 1962).
6. TIKHONOV, A. N. and SAMARSKII, A. A. Uravneniya matematicheskoi fiziki (Equations of Mathematical Physics) (Gostekhizdat, 1953).
7. TRICOMI, F. G. Lektsii po uravneniyam v chastnykh proizvodnykh (Russian translation of English title. Lectures on Partial Differential Equations) (IL, 1957).
8. BUDAK, B. M., SAMARSKII, A. A. and TIKHONOV, A. N. Sbornik zadach po matematicheskoi fizike (Collection of Problems on Mathematical Physics) (Gostekhizdat, 1956).
9. LEBEDEV, N. N., SKAL'SKAYA, I. P. and UFLYAND, YA. S. Sbornik zadach po matematicheskoi fizike (Collection of Problems on Mathematical Physics) (Gostekhizdat, 1955).
10. SMIRNOV, M. M. Zadachi po uravneniyam matematicheskoi fiziki (Problems on Equations of Mathematical Physics) (Fizmatgiz, 1961).